# 2- Amino Thiazole Nucleus: A Revisit of Biological Potential

Vikramjeet Singh
Samridhi Thakral
Pankaj Bishnoi

# 2- Amino Thiazole Nucleus: A Revisit of Biological Potential

LAP LAMBERT Academic Publishing

**Imprint**
Any brand names and product names mentioned in this book are subject to trademark, brand or patent protection and are trademarks or registered trademarks of their respective holders. The use of brand names, product names, common names, trade names, product descriptions etc. even without a particular marking in this work is in no way to be construed to mean that such names may be regarded as unrestricted in respect of trademark and brand protection legislation and could thus be used by anyone.

Cover image: www.ingimage.com

Publisher:
LAP LAMBERT Academic Publishing
is a trademark of
International Book Market Service Ltd., member of OmniScriptum Publishing Group
17 Meldrum Street, Beau Bassin 71504, Mauritius

Printed at: see last page
**ISBN: 978-613-9-45414-3**

# 2- Amino Thiazole Nucleus: A Revisit of Biological Potential

**Vikramjeet Singh**

**Samridhi Thakral**

**Pankaj Bishnoi**

# 2-Amino Thiazole Nucleus: A Revisit of Biological Potential

VIKRAMJEET SINGH, M.PHARM., Ph.D

Assistant Professor

Department of Pharmaceutical Sciences

Guru Jambheshwar University of Science & Technology

Hisar, Haryana, India, 125001


SAMRIDHI THAKRAL

B. Pharm., M. Pharm.

Department of Pharmaceutical Sciences

Guru Jambheshwar University of Science & Technology

Hisar, Haryana, India, 125001


PANKAJ BISHNOI

B. Pharm., M. Pharm.

Department of Pharmaceutical Sciences

Guru Jambheshwar University of Science & Technology

Hisar, Haryana, India, 125001

# Preface

This book is an extract of existing knowledge on 2-aminothiazole and its derivatives and will be helpful to research scholars in their research career. This includes general introduction, synthetic methods, and biological potential of 2-aminothiazoles. The literature reports describing the derivatives having 2-aminothiazole nucleus and structural features and functional groups responsible for the biological activity with mechanism of action have been compiled.

# CONTENTS

# Chapter-1

## Introduction

Heterocyclic compounds are cyclic compounds with at least one atom like N, O, S, P, Si, B and Se other than carbon in the ring and the ring itself is called a heterocycle.[1] Heterocyclic compounds are highly attractive compounds in the research and development of bioactive compounds for pharmaceutical industry. In nineteenth century (1887), thiazole ring was firstly synthesized by Rudolf Hantzch.[2] Heterocycles are divided into aromatic and saturated heterocycles and it can be further classified as four-, five-, six-, and seven-membered heterocycles.[3] There are different therapeutic uses of synthetic heterocycles like as antibacterial, anticancer, antifungal, antimycobacterial, anti-HIV, herbicidal, antidiabetic, anti-inflammatory anti-insecticidal.[4] Heterocycles carry out several essential processes inside our body, for example, nerve impulse transmission, provision of energy, metabolism, sight, transfer of hereditary information, etc., as observed by heterocyclic compounds, such as enzymes, vitamins, coenzymes, DNA, RNA, ATP and serotonin.[5]

Thiazole also known as 1,3-azole, a five membered heterocyclic compound containing one sulphur and one nitrogen atom in the ring. When 1,2-azoles are in isomeric form then nitrogen and sulphur containing compounds are known as isothiazoles.[6] Thiazole ring considered as aromatic ring according to Huckel'srule, delocalization of a lone pair of electrons take place from the sulfur atom for necessity of $6\pi$ electrons. The resonance forms are:

Sulfur can attain both $\sigma$ and $\pi$ bond characters so the investigation of its binding interaction with receptor moiety is also a fascinating field of research during last decades. The example of several natural and synthetic bioactive compounds that contains thiazole nucleus are Vitamin B such as thiamine and some antibiotics drugs like micrococcin, penicillin and various metabolic products of primitive marine animal and fungi respectively.[7] Heterocycles compounds containing thiazole nucleus were reported to have several bioactivities like antiviral, anti-HIV, antitumor, antihypertensive, antifungal, anti-inflammatory, anticonvulsion and some derivatives are known for their pesticides, herbicidal and insecticidal properties.[8-10] Some of the examples of drugs containing thiazole derivatives are Tiazofurin and Bleomycin as antineoplastic agents, Nizatidine as antiulcer agent, Ritonavir as anti-HIV drug, Imidacloprid as insecticide.[11]

## History of thiazole

The work of Hoffman on benzothiazoles in 1879 led to the systemic study of parent heterocyclic and its derivatives in 1887 by Hantzsch.[6] The thiazole molecule has aromatic character and initates pyridine in most of its physical and chemical properties. The classical structure (I) with fixed double bonds at 2,3- and 4,5-positions was suggested in 1920.[12]

$$\underset{1}{\overset{\overset{\displaystyle 4 \frown N \, 3}{5 \left\langle \,\,\, \right\rangle 2}}{S}}$$

(I)

The impact of electrophilic and nucleophilic reagents on thiazole and its derivatives was suggested by Roberts in 1947 and can be represented by resonance structures (II) and (III) derived from structure (I) without recourse to the resonance involving the sulfur atom.

II          III

In 2006, 2-amino-1,3-selenazoles was synthesized from selenourea in water using β-cyclodextrin as a catalyst and in 2008, Potewar and co-worker reported the synthesis of 2-aminothiazole analogues in water for 1-2 h.[13]

2-Aminothiazole, is a heterocyclic amine featuring thiazoleas a core nucleus. It is soluble in alcohols, water and diethyl ether and possesses an odor like pyridine.[14]

2-Aminothiazoles are used in cotton industries as disperse dyes from decades. 2-Aminothiazole containing drugs are used for the treatment of peptic ulcer, pneumonia, tonsillitis, chronic bronchitis, inflammation, cancer, diabetes, microbial and mycobacterial infections.[15] 2-Aminothiazoles are also reported for the cure of neurological diseases as potential neuroprotective agents and for Huntington's disease as modulators of transcriptional repression.[16]

# References

1. Garcia-Valverde M, Torroba T. Sulfur-Nitrogen heterocycles. Molecules 2005;10:318-320.

2. Al-Shamkhani ZAN, Al-Hazam HA. Microwave assisted synthesis, characterizations and antibacterial activity of some of thiazole derivatives. Res J Pharm Biol Chem Sci. 2015;6(2):718-725.

3. Joule A J, Mills K, 2010. Heterocyclic chemistry. Fifth edition, Chapter 25, John Wiley and Sons: 461.

4. Gupta V, Kant V. A review on biological activity of imidazole and thiazole moieties and their derivatives. SciInt. 2013;1(7): 253-260.

5. Mishra BB, Kumar D, Mishra A, Mohapatra PP, Tiwari VK. Cyclo-release strategy in solid-phase combinatorial synthesis of heterocyclic skeletons. Adv Heterocycl Chem. 2012;107:41-99.

6. Prajapati AK, Modi VP. Synthesis and biological activity of N-{5-(4-methylphenyl) diazenyl-4-phenyl-1, 3-thiazol-2-yl} benzamide derivatives. Quim Nova. 2011;34(5): 771-774.

7. Kouhkan M, Souldozi A, Talebi R. In vitro antimicrobial activity of new substituted phenylthiazole derivatives. Iranian J Toxicol. 2018;12(1):33-37.

8. Li JR, Li DD, Wang RR, Sun J, Dong JJ, Du QR, Fang F, Zhang WM, Zhu HL. Design and synthesis of thiazole derivatives as potent FabH inhibitors with antibacterial activity. Eur J Med Chem. 2014;75:438-447.

9. Narayana B, Raj KV, Ashalatha BV, Kumari NS, Sarojini BK. Synthesis of some new 5-(2-substituted-1, 3-thiazol-5-yl)-2-hydroxy benzamides and their 2-alkoxy derivatives as possible antifungal agents. Eur J Med Chem. 2004;39(10):867-872.

10. Bharti SK, Nath G, Tilak R, Singh SK. Synthesis, anti-bacterial and anti-fungal activities of some novel Schiff bases containing 2, 4-disubstituted thiazole ring. Eur J Med Chem. 2010;45(2):651-660.

11. Kumar P. Study of synthesis and biological importance of thiazole (heterocyclic compound). Orient J Chemistry. 2013;29(3):1225-1231.

12. Facchinetti V, Avellar M M, Nery A C S, Gomes C R B, Vasconcelos T R A, de SouzaM V N. Synthesis. 2016;48:437–440.

13. Gallardo-Godoy A, Gever J, Fife K L, Silber B M, Prusiner S B, Renslo A R. J Med Chem. 2011;54:1010–1021.

14. Das D, Sikdar P, Bairagi M. Recent developments of 2-aminothiazoles in medicinal chemistry. Eur J Med Chem. 2016;109:89-98.

15. Singh N, Sharma U S, Sutar N, Kumar S, Sharma U K. Synthesis and antimicrobial activity of some novel 2-amino thiazole derivatives. J Chem Pharm Res. 2010;2(3):691-698.

# Chapter- 2

## Synthesis of 2-aminothiazoles

***2.1. The Hantzsch thiazole synthesis-***Thiazole derivatives were synthesized by the reaction of thiomide and haloketone in the presence of methanol or ethanol.[1]

***2.2. Gabriel synthesis-*** The 2,5-disubstituted thiazole were synthesized by the reaction of an acylamino-ketone with phosphorus pentasulfide.[2]

***2.3. Conventional synthesis of 2-aminothiazole-*** Firstly reaction of ethyl acetoacetate and N-bromosuccinimide (NBS) in dichloromethane yielded ethyl 2-bromo-3-oxobutanoteas an intermediate and further reaction was carried out with thiourea and obtained ethyl 2-amino-4-methyl thiazole-5-carboxylate.[3]

***2.4. The Cook-Heilbronthiazole synthesis-*** The Cook-Heilbron synthesized 5-amino-2-mercaptothiazole through the reaction of α-amino nitriles with carbon disulphide.[2]

**2.5. Microwave irradiation synthesis-** 2-Aminothiazole was synthesized through the reaction of acetophenone with thiourea and iodine with 90W in microwave oven and the concentrated liquid ammonia was used for the end of reaction.[4]

*Mechanism of reaction-* Firstly phenyl iodide was formed by nucleophilic attack of amine group of thiourea at the carbon atom of carbonyl group, the second step occurred when second nucleophilic attack of sulphur of thiourea and the carbon carrying iodide group eliminating the iodide in the end of the reaction.[4]

**2.6.** Substituted 2-aminothiazoles were synthesized by reaction of α-nitro-epoxide and cyanamide in the existence of sulfide reagent ($Na_2S.9H_2O$) in n-propanol at room temperature without any additives.[5]

**2.7.**2-Amino-4-substituted-thiazoles were obtained via the reaction of ketones with formamidinedisulfide dihydrobromide.[6]

$$RCHOCH_3 + \left(SC=NH_2\ Br\right)_2 \xrightarrow{-H_2O} \quad \text{(thiazole·HBr)} + H_2N\overset{+}{C}=NH_2\ \overset{-}{Br}$$

**2.8.**2-Amino thiazole was synthesized via one-pot synthesis through the reaction of thiourea with phenacyl bromide in the presence of tetrahydrofuran and get 4-phenylthiazol-2-amine.[7]

$$\text{(phenacyl bromide)} + H_2N\overset{S}{\underset{}{C}}NH_2 \xrightarrow{THF} \text{(4-phenylthiazol-2-amine)}$$

**2.9.**The cyclocondensation reaction was used to obtain 2-aminothiazole via the reaction of α-tosyloxy ketones and thiourea at room temperature by using PEG-400 [poly (ethylene glycol-400)] in the existence of sodium carbonate.[1]

$$Ar\overset{O}{\underset{}{C}}OTs + H_2N\overset{S}{\underset{}{C}}NH_2 \xrightarrow[PEG-400]{Na_2CO_3} \text{(Ar-thiazol-NH}_2\text{)}$$

**2.10.**2-Aminothiazoles were synthesized by one-pot reaction of ketone and thiourea using biodegradable green catalyst nanochitosan.[1]

$$R_1\overset{O}{\underset{}{C}}R_2 + H_2N\overset{S}{\underset{}{C}}NH_2 \xrightarrow[Reflux, EtOH]{Nanochitosan, I_2} \text{(R}_1\text{,R}_2\text{-thiazol-NH}_2\text{)}$$

**2.11.**2-Aminothaizole was obtained by the reaction of various aldehyde with aqueous hydrobromic acid and hydrogen peroxide solution and the intermediate was further reacted with thiourea derivatives and furnished the desired 2-aminothiazole derivatives.[8]

$$R\overset{O}{\underset{}{C}}H \xrightarrow[H_2O]{\substack{HBR \\ H_2O_2}} \left[R\overset{O}{\underset{Br}{C}}H\right] \xrightarrow{H_2N\overset{S}{\underset{}{C}}N_H^{R'}} \text{(R-thiazol-N}_H^{R'}\text{)}$$

***2.12.*Miscellaneous Methods-**2-Amino-4-phenylthiazole was synthesized by the reaction of diazoacetophenone with thiourea.[9]

$$PhCOCH_2N_2 \ + \ H_2NCSNH_2 \longrightarrow \underset{Ph}{\overset{S}{\Longleftarrow}}NH_2 \ + \ N_2 \ + \ H_2O$$

***2.13.*2,4-Diaminothiazole was synthesized by the condensation reaction of halogeno-nitriles and thiourea.

$$NC\text{-}CH_2Cl \ + \ H_2NCSNH_2 \xrightarrow{\text{-HNR}_2} \underset{H_2N}{\overset{S}{\Longleftarrow}}NH_2$$

# References

1. Jain N, Singh B. An overview of biological and synthetic aspects of thiazole derivatives in heterocyclic chemistry. *World J*Res Rev. 2016;3(5):52-57.

2. Ayati A, Emami S, Asadipour A, Shafiee A, Foroumadi A. Recent alications of 1, 3-thiazole core structure in the identification of new lead compounds and drug discovery. Eur J Med Chem. 2015;97:699-718.

3. Meng G, Wang M, Zheng A, Dou J, Guo Z. Efficient one-pot synthesis of ethyl-2-substitued-4-methylthiazole-5-carboxylates. Green   Chem   Lett Rev. 2014;7(1): 46-49.

4. Al-Shamkhani Z A N, Al-Hazam H A. Microwave assisted synthesis, characterizations and antibacterial activity of some of thiazole derivatives. Res JPharm Biol Chem Sci. 2015;6(2):718-725.

5. Guo S, Zhao D, Zhu Y, Yu Y, Chen W, Zhang G. One-pot three-component protocol for the synthesis of substituted 2-aminothiazoles. Synth Commun, 2017;47(19):1758-1764.

6. Metwally M A, Abdel-Latif E, Amer F A, Kau G. Versatile 2-amino-4-substituted-1, 3-thiazoles: synthesis   and   reactions. J   Sulfur Chem. 2004;25(1): 63-85.

7. Mishra B B, Kumar D, Mishra A, Mohapatra P P, Tiwari V K. Cyclo-release strategy in solid-phase combinatorial synthesis of heterocyclic skeletons. Adv Heterocycl Chem. 2012;107:41-99.

8. Rajendiran C, Nagarajan P, Chary M T. Eco-friendly water as a solvent for the one-pot synthesis of 2-aminothiazoles. J Chem Pharm Res. 2016;8(2):813-820.

9. King L C, Hlavacek RJ. J Am Chem Soc.1950;72:3722.

# Chapter-3

## Antimicrobial activity of 2-aminothiazoles

A microorganism or microbe is a unicellular or small multicellular organism including bacteria, protozoa, fungi, viruses and their microbial infections are become a serious health problem. The medicine or drug that kills and inhibits the growth of microorganism is known as antimicrobial agent.[1]Antimicrobial resistance occurs when microorganisms such as bacteria, fungi, viruses and parasites change in ways that render the medications used to cure the infections they cause ineffective. Antimicrobial resistance (AMR) is a widely recognized and growing problem, AMR causes more than 7,00,000 deaths each year worldwide and in case of new born more than 60,000 died each year in India. It is estimated that more than 30,000 women die each year as a result of severe infections when giving birth.[2] 2-Aminothiazole is a significant and important scaffold which is practiced in different branch of chemistry and examples of 2-aminothiazole containing drugs are such as Abafungin as an antifungal and Sulfathiazole as antimicrobial agent.[3] The different type of bacteria has become resistant to a large number of antibiotics, including third generation cephalosporins and carbapenems.

Sulfathiazole

Abafungin

Zhang et al. (2017) synthesized two series of newer urea- and amide-functionalized 2,4-disubstituted thiazole derivatives and broth micro dilution assay method was used for evaluating antimicrobial activity. Compounds **1a, 1b, 2** displayed excellent in vitro antibacterial activity towards *Bacillus subtilis, Staphylococcus aureus, Pseudomonas aeruginosa, Escherichia coli* as compared to standard drug Ciprofloxacin. On the bases of SAR (structure activity relationship) study, it was found that the halogen group such as fluoro or chloro increased the antibacterial activity.[4]

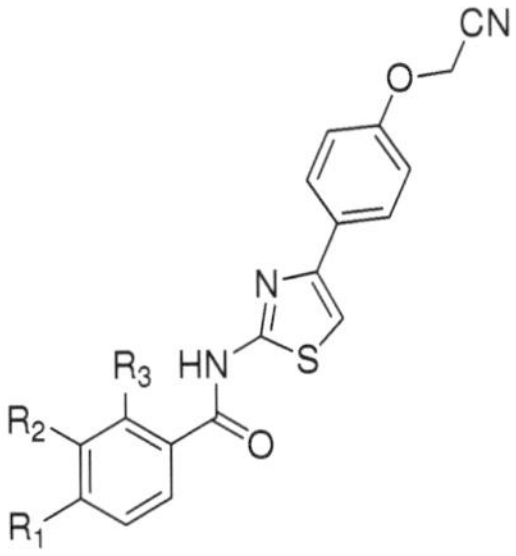

1(a-b)

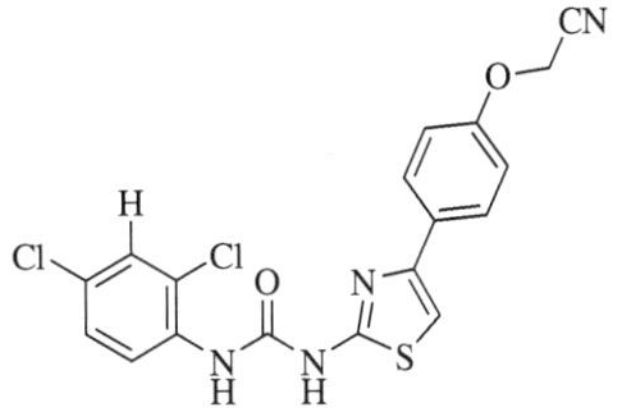

2

| Comp. | 1a | 1b | 2 |
|---|---|---|---|
| $R_1$ | F | H | Cl |
| $R_2$ | H | F | H |
| $R_3$ | H | H | Cl |

Desai et al.(2016) reported novel thiazole-based 1,3,4-oxadiazole analogues and evaluated them for their antimicrobial potential against *Streptococcus pyogenes*, *E. coli*, *P. aeruginosa*, *S. aureus*, *C. albicans*, *A. niger* and *A. clavatus*. Compounds **3a** and **3b** containing 4-OCH$_3$ and 4-CH$_3$ groups displayed the highest inhibition towards *S. aureus* and *S. pyogenes* and compound **3c** showed higher inhibitory activity towards all fungal strains.[5]

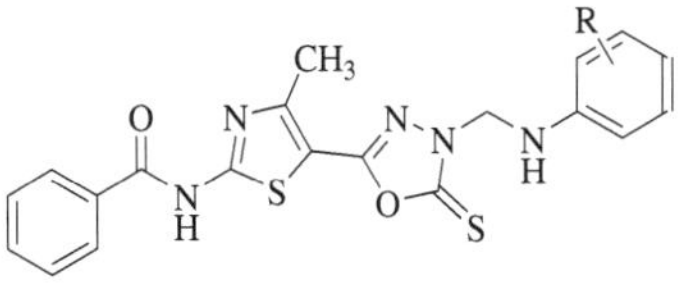

3 (a-c)

| Comp. | R |
|---|---|
| 3a | -4-OCH$_3$ |
| 3b | -4-CH$_3$ |
| 3c | -4-F |

Kaur et al. (2016) synthesized oxazolidone-thiazole hybrid derivatives. These compounds displayed the antioxidant, antimicrobial and ultraviolet mediated DNA damage protective activity. Compounds **4 (a-c)** displayed excellent antibacterial and antifungal activity towards *B. subtilis*, *S. cerevisiae*, *C. albicans* as compared to reference drugs. The SAR results indicated that compounds having biphenyl substituents and also bearing halo-substituent in order 2-fluorophenyl>3-chlorophenyl>4-fluorophenyl>4-chlorophenyl>4-bromophenyl showed the highest antibacterial activity but in case of an antifungal activity, compounds having 2-naphthyl substitution and also bearing halo-substituent in order 4-chlorophenyl>4-fluorophenyl>4-bromophenyl>2-fluorophenyl displayed excellent activity.[6]

| Comp. | Ar |
|---|---|
| 4a | |
| 4b | |
| 4c | |

4 (a-c)

Ansari et al. (2017) described a series of new quionolinepyrazoline-based coumarinylthiazole derivatives and screened for its antibacterial activity towards *E. faecalis, S. aureus,S. epidermidis, B. subtilis, B. cereus* and antifungal activity towards *A. niger, C. albicans* and *M. purpureous*. The SAR results indicated that compounds (**5a** and **5b**) bearing fluoro substituent displayed the most potent antimicrobial activity. The compounds **5a** and **5b** also exhibited better antifungal activity as compared to reference drug ketoconazole against *Penicillium citrinum*.[7]

| Comp. | 5a | 5b |
|---|---|---|
| R | Cl | F |
| $R_1$ | F | F |

5 (a-b)

Gjorgjieva et al. (2016) reported novel benzothiazole derivatives which displayed inhibitory activity towards DNA gyrase and topoisomerase IV from both *S. aureus and E. coli*. Compounds **6a** and **6b** displayed highest antibacterial activity.

*Mode of Action-* Compounds **6a** and **6d** were found to have inhibition potential against DNA gyrase and molecular docking study also revealed that compound showed antibacterial potential by displaying ATP-binding site of interaction with *E. coli* DNA gyrase B (PDB:4DUH).[8]

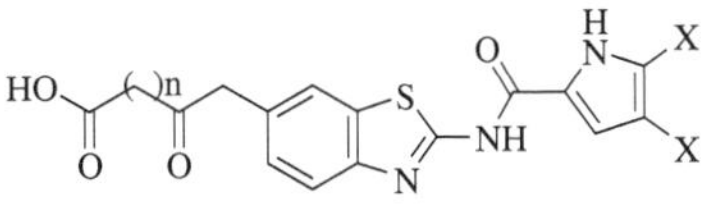

| Comp. | 6a | 6b |
|-------|-----|-----|
| X | Cl | Br |
| N | 0 | 0 |

6 (a-b)

Hagras et al. (2017) reported the phenylthiazoles as promising scaffold and evaluated their antibacterial potential targeting vancomycin- and methicillin-resistant *S. aureus*. On the basis of SARs of phenylthiazoles, a nitrogenous and a lipophilic component were reported as two essential structural features which are crucial for antibacterial activity. Pyrimidine ring with a nitrogen part appeared with a prolonged half-life, while the biphenyl moiety admitted the more potent analogue **7** and compounds **8a**, **8b** and **8c** displayed excellent anti-MRSA activity.[9]

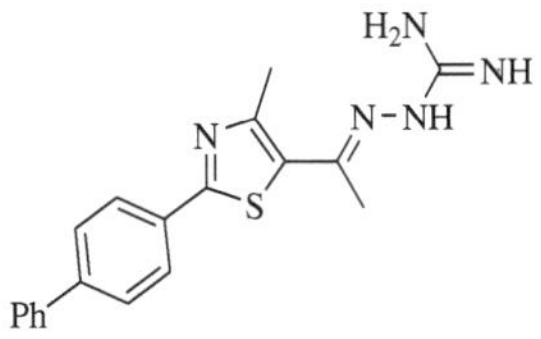

7 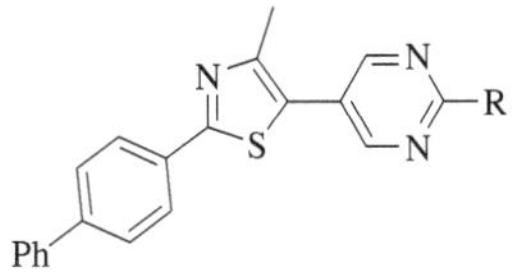                    8 (a-c)

| Comp. | R |
|-------|---|
| 8a | 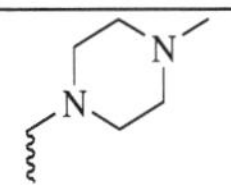 |
| 8b | 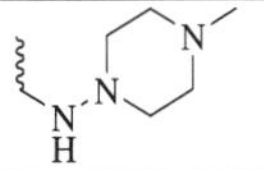 |
| 8c | 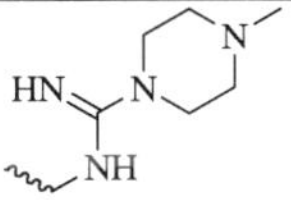 |

Karegoudar et al. (2008) presented a new series of 4-aryl/chloroalkly-2-(2,3,5-trichlorophenyl)-1,3-thiazoles and evaluated for their antimicrobial potential. It was established that compounds **9a**, **9b**, **10a**, **10b**, **11a**, **11b** with different substituents like as (**9a/11b**-(4-methylthio) phenyl, **9b/11a**-(salicylamide) displayed the most potent antibacterial activity as compared to standard drug Ciprofloxacin, whereas compounds **9c, 9d, 10c** and **11 (c-e)** exhibited the highest antifungal activity.[10]

9 (a-d)          10 (a-c)          11 (a-e)

| Comp. | Ar/R | Comp. | Ar/R |
|-------|------|-------|------|
| 9a | 4-SCH3-C6H4 | 10c | Piperidino |
| 9b | 4-OH-3-CONH2- C6H4 | 11a | 4-OH-3-CONH2- C6H4 |
| 9c | 3-Pyridyl | 11b | 4-SCH3-C6H4 |
| 9d | Biphenyl | 11c | 3-Pyridyl |
| 10a | N-Methylpiperazino | 11d | 4-NO2- C6H4 |
| 10b | Morpholino | 11e | 4-OCH3.C6H4 |

Li et al. (2014) synthesized a new series of compounds via the reaction of 4-(4-bromophenyl) thiazol-2-amine or 4-phenylthiazol-2-amine with aromatic acid and screened for its antibacterial activities towards *P. aeruginosa, E. coli, B. subtilis* and *S. aereus* as compared to the reference drug Kanamycin B and Penicillin G. Compounds **12a, 12b, 12c, 12d** displayed highest antibacterial activity.

*Mode of Action*- Compound **12e** was found to have inhibition potential against *E. coli* FabH and molecular docking study also revealed that compound showed antibacterial potential by displaying strong binding interaction with FabH protein (PDB:31L9).[11]

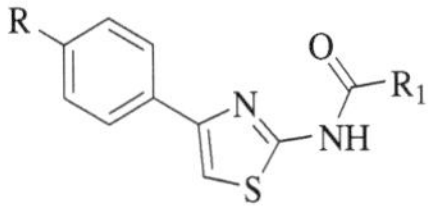

| Comp. | R | R₁ |
|-------|---|-----|
| 12a | H | 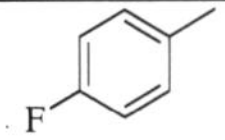 |
| 12b | H | 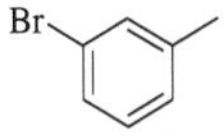 |
| 12c | Br | 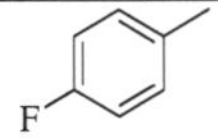 |
| 12d | Br | 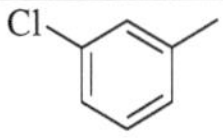 |
| 12e | Br | 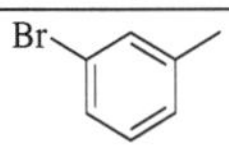 |

12 (a-e)

Liaras et al. (2014) syntheiszed a novel series of thiazole-based aminopyrimidines and N-phenylpyrazoline and investigated its antibacterial activity towards Gram positive and Gram negative bacteria. Compounds **13a** and **14** displayed the highest antibacterial activity whereas compound **13b** exhibited excellent antifungal activity towards *A. ochaceus* and *A. versicolor*.[12]

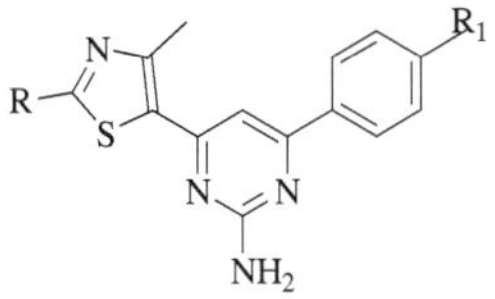

13 (a-b)

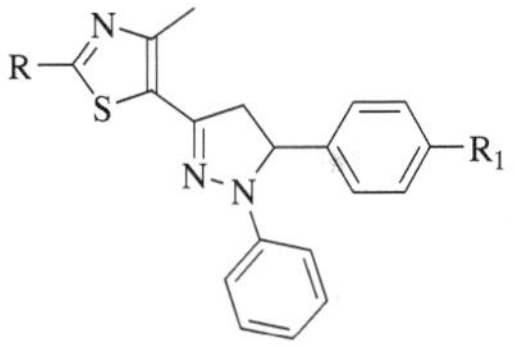

14

| Comp. | R | R₁ | Comp. | R | R₁ |
|-------|------|-----|-------|-------|-----|
| 13a | Ph | H | 14a | NHCH₃ | 4-F |
| 13b | NHCH₃ | H | | | |

Narayana et al. (2004) synthesized a novel series of 5-(2-substituted-1,3-thiazol-5-yl)-2-hydroxy benzamide analogues and investigated for its antifungal activity against *A. fumigatus, A. flavus, C.albicans, Trichophyton mentagrophyte* sand *Penicillium marneffei* by serial dilution method. Compound 5-[(2-(3-chlorophenyl)-1,3-thiazol-5yl]-2-butoxy benzamide (**15**) was found to have potential towards all tested microorganisms, although compound **16** showed moderate antimicrobial activity.[13]

15                                                                 16

| Comp. | 15 | 16 |
|-------|----|----|
| $R_1$ | -NH-3-Cl-$C_6H_5$ | -$C_6H_5$ |
| $R_2$ | Butyl | - |

Cui et al. (2016) presented a series of new 3-aminothiazolquinolones in an effort to avoid quinolone resistance. Compound 3-(2-aminothiazol-4-yl)-7-chloro-6-(pyrrolidin-1-yl) quinolone **17** displayed excellent antibacterial activity. On the bases of SARs, it was found that the 2-aminothiazole fragment at $3^{rd}$ position of quinolone displayed excellent role in expending antibacterial activity.

*Mode of Action-* Compound **17** was found to have inhibition potential against DNA gyrase and molecular docking study also revealed that compound showed antibacterial potential by displaying water-metal ion bridge to initiate irreparable DNA breakage which eventually leads to bacterial cell death(PDB:2XCT). [14]

17

| Comp. | 17 |
|-------|----|
| N | 0 |
| X | C |

Padmavathi et al. (2011) presented a novel series of amido linked pyrazolyl/pyrrolyl-oxazoles, thiazole and imidazole bis heterocycles by 1,3-dipolar cycloadditon of diazomethane and TosMIC to the corresponding cinnamamide derivatives. Compounds **18a** and **19a** exhibited excellent antifungal activity towards *P. chrysogenum* and *P. aeruginosa*. Compounds **18b, 20a, 19b** having

16

thiazole ring showed the highest antibacterial activities towards *B. subtillis* as compared to compound **18c**, **20b**, **19c** having oxazole unit.[15]

18 (a-c)          19 (a-b)          20 (a-c)

| Comp. | 18a | 18b | 18c | 19a | 19b | 19c | 20a | 20b |
|-------|-----|-----|-----|-----|-----|-----|-----|-----|
| X | NH | S | O | NH | S | O | S | O |
| AR | 4-Cl.Ph | Ph | Ph | 4-Cl.Ph | Ph | Ph | Ph | Ph |

Thumar et al. (2009) synthesized 4-(4-subtituted phenyl)-2-aminothiazoles by the solid phase reaction of thiourea, substituted acetophenones, and iodine. Results demonstrated that compounds **21a,21b**, **21c** and **21d** displayed valuable antibacterial activity towards *S. aureus* and *B. subtilis* bacteria whereas compound **22** showed excellent activity towards *E. coli* bacterial species. It was also found that compounds **21e**, **23a** and **23b** had excellent antifungal activity towards *A. niger*.[16]

21 (a-e)          22          23 (a-b)

| Comp. | R | Comp. | R | R₁ |
|-------|---|-------|---|----|
| 21a | H | 21e | Br | - |
| 21b | Cl | 22 | CH₃ | - |
| 21c | OCH₃ | 23a | OCH₃ | COOC₂H₅ |
| 21d | CH₃ | 23b | Cl | COOC₂H₅ |

Turan-Zitouniet al. (2003) synthesized 2-[(benzazole-2-yl) thioacetylamino]thiazole derivatives by the reaction of 4-methyl-2-(chlororacetylamino) thiazole derivatives with benzazol-2-thiole in acetone in the presence of $K_2CO_3$. Compound **24a** showed highest antimicrobial activity towards *S. aureus, E. coli, B. subtilis, S. faecium, S. epidermidis* but compound **24b** is one which displayed excellent activity towards *C. albicans*.[17]

| Comp. | R | $R_1$ |
|-------|---|-------|
| 24a | H | Cl |
| 24b | H | $NO_2$ |

24 (a-b)

Lu et al. (2012) reported a novel series of 4-(2,6-dichlorobenzyloxy) phenyl thiazole, imidazole and oxazole analogues and evaluated for antibacterial and antitubercular activity. The thiazole compound **25a** having p-chlorobenzoyl substitution displayed the highest antitubercular activity towards *Mycobacterium tuberculosis*. On the bases of SARs, it was found that compounds **25b, 25c, 26 (a-b)** and **26 (c-d)** displayed excellent antibacterial activity towards *S. aureus, E. coli, S. pneumoniae and Penicillin-resistant S. pneumoniae*.[18]

25 (a-c)                    26 (a-d)

| Comp. | $R_1$ |
|-------|-------|
| 25a | 4-Cl-Ph |
| 25b | Ph |
| 25c | Ethylene |
| 26a | Ph |
| 26b | 4-Cl-Ph |
| 26c | 4-CH₃O-Ph |
| 27d | n-Pr |

Rostom et al. (2014) reported the bifunctional ethyl 2-amino-4-methylthiazole-5-carboxylate analogues and screened them for in vitro anticancer and antimicrobial activity. The SAR results indicated that compounds **27a** (with R-C₆H₅), **28a** (with R-C₆H₅), **28b** (having R-4-CH₃-C₆H₄) and **28c** (bearing 4-fluorophenyl moiety) displayed highest antibacterial activity towards *S. aureus* and *B. subtilis* and displayed weak antifungal activity towards *C. albicans*. On another side compounds **27b** and **29** showed more potent anticancer activity.[19]

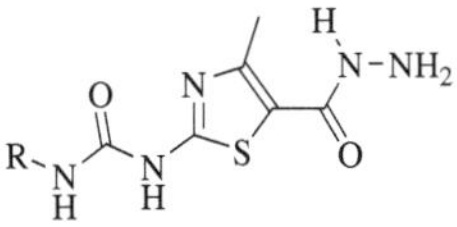

27 (a-b) 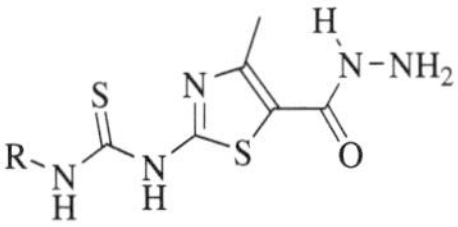    28 (a-c) 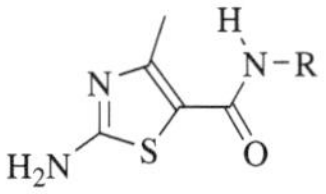    29

| Comp. | R | Comp. | R |
|-------|---|-------|---|
| 27a | $C_6H_5$ | 28b | 4-$CH_3$-$C_6H_4$ |
| 27b | Cyclo-$C_6H_{11}$ | 28c | 4-F-$C_6H_4$ |
| 28a | $C_6H_5$ | 29 | $(CH_2)_2OH$ |

Taile et al. (2010) reported 2-(substituted benzylideneamino)-4-(4'-hydroxy phenyl) thiazoles derivatives and investigated their antibacterial activity towards *Klebsiella aerogens, E. coli, S. aureus* and *B. subtilis*. Compounds **30a, 30b, 31a, 31b, 31c** displayed highest antibacterial as well as antifungal activity.[20]

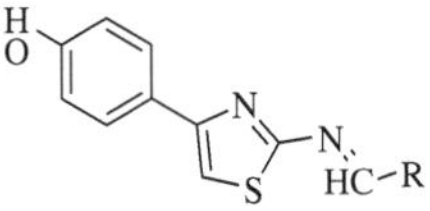

30 (a-b)

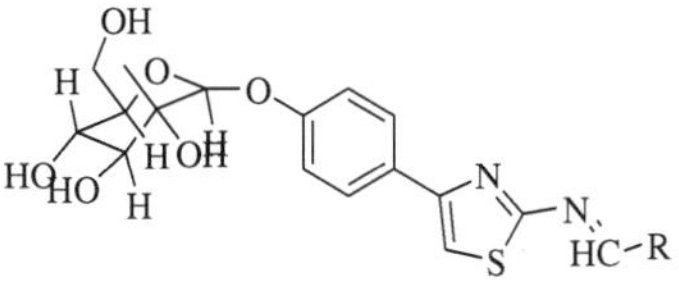

31 (a-c)

| Comp. | 30a | 30b | 31a | 31b | 31c |
|-------|-----|-----|-----|-----|-----|
| R | Phenyl | p-Flouro aryl | Phenyl | p-Flouro aryl | 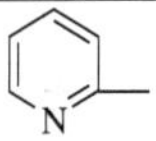 |

Abdel-Wahabet al. (2011) investigatednovel thiazole and pyrazoline heterocycle having 2-thienylpyrazole moiety by using 1-Phenyl-3-(thiophen-2-yl)-1H-pyrazole-4-carbaldehyde as a synthon. Compound **32** displayed excellent antibacterial and antifungal activity towards *A. niger*. On the basis of structure-activity relationship, it was found that compound **33** containing flourine substituent and compound **32** with 4-thiazolidinone displayed highest anti-inflammatory and analgesic activity.[21]

32                                              33

Elsebaei et al. (2018) synthesized the alkynyl-containing phenylthiazoles and screened their antibacterial activity towards *Methicillin-resistant S. aureus* (MRSA). The compound phenylethynyl derivatives **34a, 34b** and **34c** by changing the terminal phenyl ring with moieties exhibited most potent antibacterial activity towards MRSA.

*Mode of Action-* These compound exhibited antibacterial activity by inhibiting undecaprenyl diphosphate phosphatase and undecaprenyl diphosphate synthase which serves as a lipid carrier for peptidoglycan synthesis and thus interfering with bacterial cell wall synthesis.[22]

34 (a-c)

| Comp. | 34a | 34b | 34c |
|---|---|---|---|
| R | | | |

Bharti et al. (2010) reported a series of arylidene-2-(-(4-methoxy/bromophenyl)thiazol-2-yl) hydrazine and 1-(4-(4-methoxy/bromophenyl)thiazol-2-yl)-2-cyclohexylidene/ cyclopentylidene hydrazine derivatives which displayed antibacterial as well as antifungal activity. Compounds **35a, 35b, 35c, 35d, 35e, 35f** and **35g** displayed the more potent antibacterial activity towards *S. aureus* and *V. cholerae*. On the other hand, compounds **35h, 35i, 35d, 35j, 35g, 35a, 35b, 36a** and **36b** displayed broad spectrum antifungal activity whereas compound **35i** and **35d** displayed excellent activity towards *A. flavus, C. neoformans, C. albicans* and *C. tropicum*. Study demonstrated that compounds possessing substitution of cyclohexanimine/ cyclopentaniminyl at C-8 position displayed more potent antifungal activity.[23]

| 35 (a-j) | | | 36 (a-b) | | 37 (a-b) |

| Comp. | R | R₁ | R₂ | Comp. | R | R₁ | R₂ |
|---|---|---|---|---|---|---|---|
| 35a | H | | -OCH₃ | 35h | H | | -OCH₃ |
| 35b | H | | -OCH₃ | 35i | H | | -OCH₃ |
| 35c | H | | -OCH₃ | 35j | H | | -Br |
| 35d | | | -OCH₃ | 36a | - | - | -OCH₃ |
| 35e | H | | -Br | 36b | - | - | -Br |
| 35f | H | | -Br | 37a | - | - | -OCH₃ |
| 35g | | | -Br | 37b | - | - | -Br |

Praveen et al. (2014) synthesized a novel series of N-[4-(substituted)-1,3-thiazol-2-yl]-2-(substituted)acetamide and methyl 2-(2-(2-(substituted) acetamido) thiazol-4-yl) acetate derivatives and screened its antibacterial activity towards *S. aureus, E. coli, P. aeruginosa, K. pneumoniae* and antifungal activity towards *T. mentagrophytes, P. marneffei, A. fumigates* and *A. flavus*. Compounds such as **38a, 38b, 38c,** and **38d** displayed highest antibacterial potential whereas compounds **38e, 38a, 38f, 38g, 38h, 38i** and **38j** exhibited excellent antifungal activity.[24]

38 (a-j)

| Comp. | R₂ | R₃ | Comp. | R₂ | R₃ |
|---|---|---|---|---|---|
| 38a | -CH₃ | | 38f | -CH₃ | |
| 38b | -CH₃ | | 38g | Cl | |

| 38c | Cl | 38h | Cl |
| 38d | | 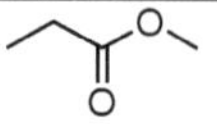 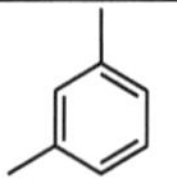 38i 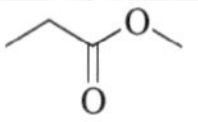 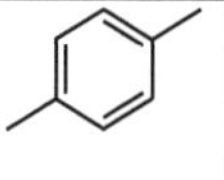 | |
| 38e | 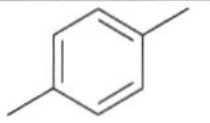 -CH₃ | 38j 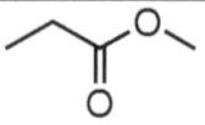 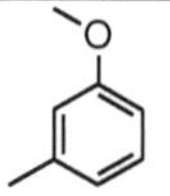 | |

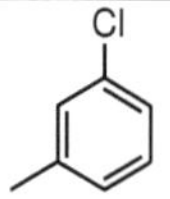

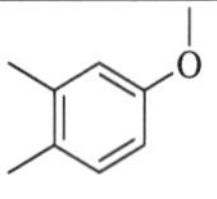

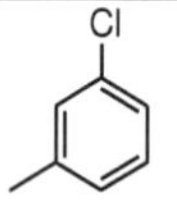

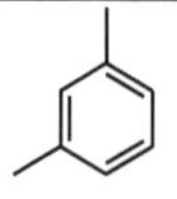

Badiger et al. (2013) reported a series of 4-(2-chloro-4-fluorophenyl)-5-(4-substituted phenylsulfanyl)-thiazole-2-ylamines/acetamides and 5-(4-substituted benzenesulfonyl)-4-(2-chloro-4-fluorophenyl)-thiazole-2-ylamines/acetamide derivatives and screened for its antibacterial potential towards *E. coli, methicillin resistant S. aureus* bacteria and antifungal activity towards *A. niger* and *C .albicans*. Compounds **39** and **40** having acetylamino group with chloro substituent exhibited the most potent activity.[25]

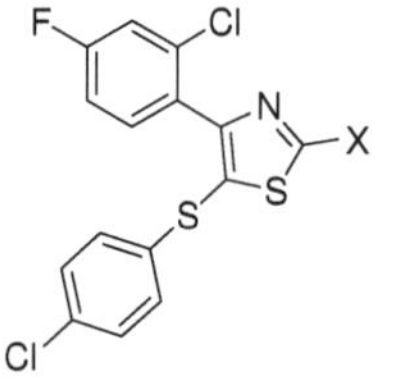

X: NHCOCH₃

39 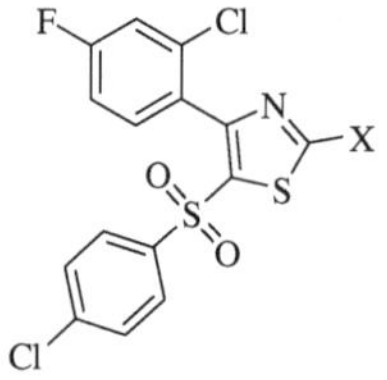        40

Shiran et al. (2015) presented a series of 2, 2'-(1,4-phenylene)-bis-(3-aryl-2-imino-4-aryl-3H-thiazole) and 3-alkyl-2-(arylimino)-4-cyclopropyl-5-(2'-fluorophenyl)-thiazole analogues and evaluated its antibacterial activity. Compound **41a** displayed excellent antibacterial activity towards *Micrococcus luteus, Salmonella enterica* and compound **41b** exhibited inhibitory activity towards *P. aeruginosa*.[26]

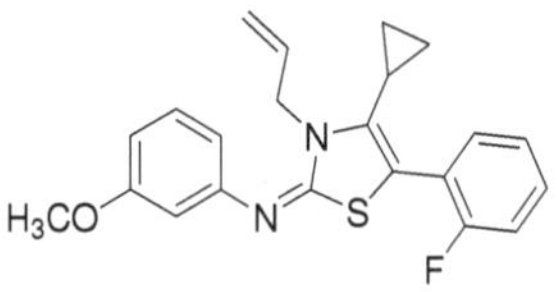

41a 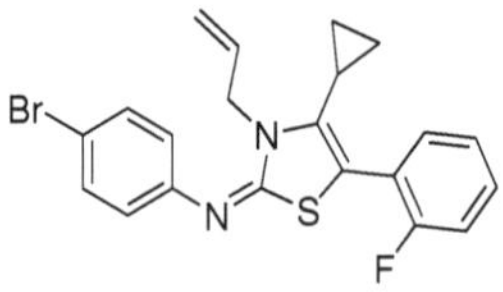        41b

22

Bondock et al. (2018) presented a novel series of functionalized 5-hetarylthiazoles which was prepared from 1-(2-allylamino-4-methylthiazol-5-yl) ethanone. These compounds were assayed for activity towards some human pathogenic microbial strains. The compounds **42a**, **42b** and **43a** displayed high antibacterial activity towards *S. pneumoniae*, whereas compounds **43a**, **43b** and **44** showed potent antifungal activity towards *A. fumigatus*. It was observed that introduction of a halogen substituent and pharmacophoric azo group at 4th position of phenyl ring increased the antimicrobial potential.[27]

42 (a-b)    43 (a-b)    44

| Comp. | R | AR |
|-------|-----|----------|
| 42a | CSNH$_2$ | 4-Cl-C$_6$H$_4$- |
| 42b | CSNHPh | 4-Cl-C$_6$H$_4$- |
| 43a | - | 4-Br-C$_6$H$_4$- |
| 43b | - | 4-F-C$_6$H$_5$- |
| 44 | - | 4-Cl-C$_6$H$_4$- |

Bhandari et al. (2016) reported a series of N-[4-(4-nitrophenoxy) phenyl]-4-(substituted)-1,3-thiazol-2-amines derivatives and investigated its antibacterial as well as anthelmintic activity. Compound (**45a**) N-[4-(4-nitrophenoxy) phenyl]-4-(4-methoxyphenyl)-1,3-thiazol-2-amine showed high antibacterial activity towards *P. aeruginosa, S. aureus* and *B. subtilis* and compound (**45b**) N-[4-(4-nitrophenoxy) phenyl]-4-(4-fluorophenyl)-1,3-thiazol-2-amine displayed good anthelmintic activity.[28]

45 (a-b)

| Comp. | R |
|-------|-----|
| 45a | H$_3$CO—⟨⟩— |
| 45b | F—⟨⟩— |

Abbady et al. (2015) reported some novel symmetrical diaryl selenides containing azetidin-2-onyl, thiazolyl, thiazolidin-4-onyl,glycyl and triazolin-1-yl moieties and evaluated for their antibacterial activity. The Schiff bases displayed effective minimum inhibitory concentration values than the other compounds and exhibited more antimicrobial potential. Compounds **46** with p-OCH$_3$ group and **47** with p-NO$_2$group displayed maximum antibacterial activity.[29]

| Comp. | R |
|-------|------|
| 46 | -OCH$_3$ |
| 47 | -NO$_2$ |

Abdel-Hafez et al. (2003) synthesized of novel 2-amino-4-(4'-phenylsulfanyl-phenyl)-thiazole analogues and screened for its antimicrobial activity. Compounds **48** and **49** displayed more potent antimicrobial activity towards *S. aureus, Streptoccus, P. aeruginosa* and *S. aureus*. Compounds **48, 50** and **51** also displayed excellent antifungal activity towards *P. oxalicum* and *A. parasiticus*.[30]

Kalaria et al. (2014) synthesized a novel series of bipyrazolyl thiazolone hybrids by molecular hybridization technique and investigated for their antibacterial potential. Compounds **52a, 52b** and **52c** containing thiophene moiety and compounds having furan moiety such as **53a** and **53b** displayed highest antibacterial activity towards *B. subtilis* and *S. aureus*.

24

*Mode of Action*-Compound **54** was found to have inhibition potential against *E. coli* FabH and molecular docking study also revealed that compound showed antibacterial potential by displaying strong binding interaction with FabH protein (PDB:1HNJ).[31]

52 (a-c)

53 (a-b)

54

| Comp. | Het₁ | Het |
|-------|------|-----|
| 52a | Thiophene-2-carbaldehyde | Triazole |
| 52b | Thiophene-2-carbaldehyde | Benz imidazole |
| 52c | Thiophene-2-carbaldehyde | Benztriazole |
| 53a | Furan-2-carbaldehyde | Imidazole |
| 53b | Furan-2-carbaldehyde | Benz imidazole |
| 54 | 1H-Indole-3-carbaldehyde | Benz imidazole |

Lykhin et al. (2014) presented the complex synthesis of a Pb(II) with ceftriaxone ($H_2$Ceftria) antibiotic via the reaction of lead nitrate with ceftriaxone disodium salt (hemi) heptahydrate in water-ethanol medium. It displayed antibacterial activities towards *S. aureus*, *E. coli* and *K. pneumoniae* by paper disc diffusion method. The disposition of Ceftria$^{2-}$ to Pb(II) be found over O and N of the triazine, carboxylate, lactam carbonyl and amine groups.

*Mode of Action*- Ceftriaxone formed a stable acyl-enzyme intermediate, which suppressed peptidoglycan cross-linking thus interferring the bacterial cell wall structural integrity and exhibited bactericidal activity.[32]

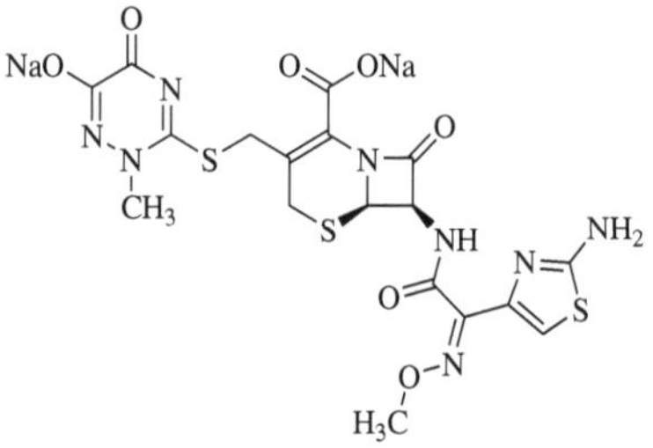

**55**

Gahtori et al. (2012) synthesized a series of chloro- and dichloro-phenylthiazolyls-triazine derivatives and screened for its antibacterial activities. Compound **56** such as 2,4-disubstituted thiazoles possessing chlorophenyl group showed excellent activities (MIC=3.125µg/ml) towards *Lactobasilluscasei* and *E. coli* than standard drugs streptomycin and penicillin, respectively. Compound **56a** and **56b** displayed more antimicrobial activity (MIC=3.125µg/ml) towards *B. cereus* as compared to reference drug penicillin (1.562 µg/ml).[33]

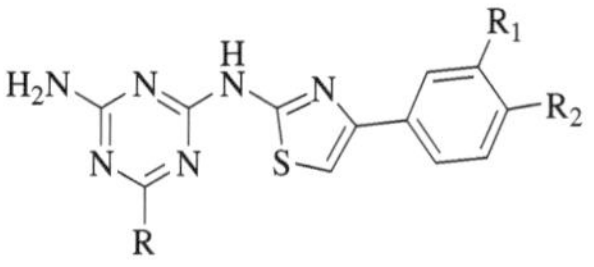

| Comp. | R | $R_1$ | $R_2$ |
|-------|---|-------|-------|
| 56a | 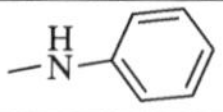 —N(H)—⟨phenyl⟩ | Cl | Cl |
| 56b | 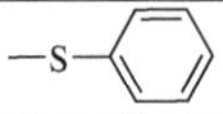 —S—⟨phenyl⟩ | Cl | Cl |

56 (a-b)

Narayana et al. (2007) reported a new series of 4-(2-chloropyridin-4-yl)-N-phenyl-1,3-thiazol-2-amines which was synthesized via reaction of substituted thioureas with (4-bromoacetyl)-2-chloropyridine. Compounds **57a** and **57b**, possessing a 3-chlorophenyl moiety demonstrated highest activity towards *S. aureus, E. coli, K. pneumoniae, P. aeruginosa* and maximum antifungal potential against *A. fumigatus, A. flavus, P. marneffei, C. albicans* and *T. mentagrophytes*.[34]

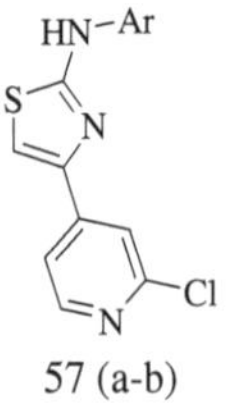

| Comp. | AR |
|-------|----|
| 57a | 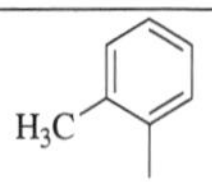 $H_3C$—⟨phenyl⟩ |
| 57b | 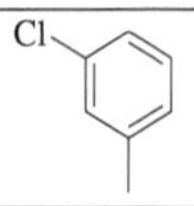 Cl—⟨phenyl⟩ |

57 (a-b)

26

Kalhor et al. (2014) reported a new series of N, N'-disubstituted thiourea, 2-amino thiazole and imidazole-2-thione analogues, in which 2-amino thiazoles was synthesized by cyclization reaction of the N, N'-disubstituted thioureas and their intermediate ketal in dilute aqueous acidic and strong acidic medium. Compounds **58a, 58b** and **58c** displayed excellent antibacterial activity towards *B. cereus, E. coli, E. faecalis, P. aeruginosa* and *S. aureus* bacteria.[35]

| Comp. | R |
|-------|------|
| 58a | 4-Cl |
| 58b | 4-Me |
| 58c | H |

58 (a-c)

Flanagan et al. (2011) presented a new series of siderophore-conjugated monocarbam compounds and evaluated its antibacterial activity towards multidrug resistant Gram negative microorganisms such as *P. aeruginosa*. The compounds **59a** and **59b** are having polar functionality on this side chain, including at least one hydrogen bond donor and **59c** having methyl group displayed highest inhibitory activity towards *P. aeruginosa* and *K. pneumoniae*.[36]

| Comp. | R₁ | R₂ |
|-------|-----|-----|
| 59a | -H | HO''' |
| 59b | -H | HO |
| 59c | -Me | HO'''—OH |

59 (a-c)

Lam et al. (2014) reported a novel series of 7-(benzimidazol-1-yl)-2,4-diaminoquinazolines for its antibacterial activity. Compound **60a** having a thiazol-2-yl group in the 2nd position of the benzimidazol displayed excellent antibacterial activity towards *S. aureus* along with compounds **60b, 60c** and **60d**.

*Mode of Action-* Compound **60a** was found to be potential inhibitor of *S. aureus* DHFR enzyme.[37]

60 (a-d)

| Comp. | 60a | 60b | 60c | 60d |
|---|---|---|---|---|
| R | | | | |
| Ar | | OCH₃ OCH₃ | OCH₃ OCH₃ | OCH₃ OCH₃ |

# References

1. Ozkay Y, Tunali Y, Karaca H, Isıkdag I. Antimicrobial activity of a new series of benzimidazole derivatives. Arc Pharmacal Res. 2011;34(9):1427.
2. WHO, Antimicrobial resistance: Global report on surveillance 2014.
3. Siddiqui N, Arshad M F, Ahsan W, Alam M S. Thiazoles: a valuable insight into the recent advances and biological activities. Int J Pharm Sci Drug Res. 2009;1(3):136-143.
4. Zhang Z H, Chen Y, Yan X J, Sun Y, Yang X M, Cai X Y, You S. Synthesis and evaluation of novel urea and amide derivatives of 2-amino-4-phenylthiazole as potential antibacterial agents. Med Chem Res. 2017;26(9): 2080-2087.
5. Desai N C, Bhatt N, Dodiya A, Karkar T, Patel B, Bhatt M. Synthesis, characterization and antimicrobial screening of thiazole based 1, 3, 4-oxadiazoles heterocycles. Res Chem Intermed. 2016;42(4): 3039-3053.
6. Kaur K, Kumar V, Beniwal V, Kumar V, Kumar N, Sharma V, Jaglan S. Synthesis of some novel oxazolidinone-thiazole hybrids as potential antimicrobial, antioxidant and UV mediated DNA damage protecting agents. Med Chem Res. 2016;25(10): 2237-2249.

7. Ansari M I, Khan SA. Synthesis and antimicrobial activity of some novel quinoline-pyrazoline-based coumarinylthiazole derivatives. Med Chem Res. 2017;26(7): 1481-1496.

8. Gjorgjieva M, Tomassic T, Baranccokova M, Katsamakas S, Ilas J, Tammela P, Peterlin M L, Kikelj D. Discovery of benzothiazole scaffold-based DNA gyrase B inhibitors. J Med Chem, 2016;59(19):8941-8954.

9. Hagras M, Mohammad H, Mandour M S, Hegazy Y A, Ghiaty A, Seleem M N, Mayhoub A S. Investigating the antibacterial activity of biphenylthiazoles against methicillin-and vancomycin-resistant Staphylococcus aureus (MRSA and VRSA). J Med Chem. 2017;60(9):4074-4085.

10. Karegoudar P, Karthikeyan M S, Prasad D J, Mahalinga M, Holla B S, Kumari N S. Synthesis of some novel 2, 4-disubstituted thiazoles as possible antimicrobial agents. Eur J Med Chem, 2008;43(2): 261-267.

11. Li J R, Li D D, Wang R R, Sun J, Dong J J, Du Q R, Fang F, Zhang W M, Zhu H L. Design and synthesis of thiazole derivatives as potent FabH inhibitors with antibacterial activity. Eur J Med Chem. 2014;75:438-447.

12. Liaras K, Geronikaki A, Glamoclija J, Ćiric A, Sokovic M. Thiazole-based aminopyrimidines and N-phenylpyrazolines as potent antimicrobial agents: Synthesis and biological evaluation. **Med Chem Commun**. 2014;5(7): 915-922.

13. Narayana B, Raj K V, Ashalatha B V, Kumari N S, Sarojini B K. Synthesis of some new 5-(2-substituted-1, 3-thiazol-5-yl)-2-hydroxy benzamides and their 2-alkoxy derivatives as possible antifungal agents. Eur J Med Chem. 2004;39(10): 867-872.

14. Cui S F, Addla D, Zhou C H. Novel 3-aminothiazolquinolones: design, synthesis, bioactive evaluation, SARs, and preliminary antibacterial mechanism. J Med Chem. 2016;59(10):4488-4510.

15. Padmavathi V, Venkatesh B C, Padmaja A. Synthesis and antimicrobial activity of amido linked pyrrolyl and pyrazolyl-oxazoles, thiazoles and imidazoles. Eur J Med Chem. 2011;46(11):5317-5326.

16. Thumar N J, Patel M P. Synthesis, characterization, and biological activity of substituted thiazole-5-carboxaldehydes and their ylidenenitriles derivatives. Phosphorus Sulfur Silicon Relat Elem. 2009;184(10): 2720-2732.

17. Turan-Zitouni G, Demirayak S, Ozdemir A, Kaplancikli Z A, Yildiz M T. Synthesis of some 2-[(benzazole-2-yl) thioacetylamino] thiazole derivatives and their antimicrobial activity and toxicity. Eur J Med Chem. 2004;39(3):267-272.

18. Lu X, Liu X, Wan B, Franzblau S G, Chen L, Zhou C, You Q. Synthesis and evaluation of anti-tubercular and antibacterial activities of new 4-(2, 6-dichlorobenzyloxy) phenyl thiazole, oxazole and imidazole derivatives. Part 2. Eur J Med Chem. 2012;49:164-171.

19. Rostom S A, Faidallah H M, Radwan M F, Badr M H. Bifunctional ethyl 2-amino-4-methylthiazole-5-carboxylate derivatives: Synthesis and in vitro biological evaluation as antimicrobial and anticancer agents. Eur J Med Chem. 2014;76:170-181.

20. Taile V S, Ingle V N, Hatzade K M. Synthesis of 2-(substituted benzylideneamino)-4-(4'-hydroxyphenyl)thiazoles and their O-glucosides. J Carbohyd Chem. 2010;29(5):207-221.

21. Abdel-Wahab B F, Abdel-Gawad H, Awad G E, Badria F A. Synthesis, antimicrobial, antioxidant, anti-inflammatory and analgesic activities of some new 3-(2'-thienyl) pyrazole-based heterocycles. Med Chem Res. 2012;21(7):1418-1426.

22. Elsebaei M M, Mohammad H, Abouf M, Abutaleb N S, Hegazy Y A, Ghiaty A, Chen L, Zhang J, Malwal S R, Oldfield E, Seleem M N. Alkynyl-containing phenylthiazoles: Systemically active antibacterial agents effective against methicillin-resistant *Staphylococcus aureus* (MRSA). Eur J Med Chem. 2018;148:195-209.

23. Bharti S K, Nath G, Tilak R, Singh S K. Synthesis, anti-bacterial and anti-fungal activities of some novel Schiff bases containing 2, 4-disubstituted thiazole ring. Eur J Med Chem. 2010;45(2):651-660.

24. Praveen A S, Yathirajan H S, Narayana B, Sarojini B K. Synthesis, characterization and antimicrobial studies of a few novel thiazole derivatives. Med Chem Res. 2014;23(1):259-268.

25. Badiger N P, Mulla J S, Khazi I, Khazi I M. Synthesis and antimicrobial activity of sulfide and sulfone derivatives of 4-(2-chloro-4-fluorophenyl)-1, 3-thiazol-2-amine/acetamide. Pharm Chem J. 2013;46(11):667-671.

26. AbbasiShiran J, Yahyazadeh A, Mamaghani M, Yamin B M, Albadi J, Shirini F, Rassa M. Novel, One-Pot, three-component, regioselective

synthesis of fluorine-containing thiazole and bis-3 H-thiazole derivatives using polyvinyl pyridine as heterogeneous catalyst, and evaluation of their antibacterial activity. Synth Commun. 2015;45(13):1520-1532.

27. Bondock S, Fouda A M. Synthesis and evaluation of some new 5-(hetaryl) thiazoles as potential antimicrobial agents. Synth Commun. 2018;48(5):561-573.

28. Bhandari N, Gaonkar S L. Anthelmintic and antibacterial screening of a new series of N-[4-(4-nitrophenoxy) phenyl]-4-(substituted)-1, 3-thiazol-2-amines. Russ J Bioorg Chem. 2016;42(2):210-214.

29. Abbady M A, Aly M M, Ismail M T, Abdel-Hafez S H. Organic selenium compounds. part ii. synthesis and antibacterial activity of some new symmetrical diarylselenides containing thiazolyl, thiazolidin-4-onyl, azetidin-2-onyl, triazolin-1-yl and glycyl moieties. Phosphorus Sulfur Silicon Relat Elem. 2015;190(11):1828-1844.

30. Abdel-Hafez S H. Synthesis, antimicrobial activity of some new 2-amino-4-(4'-phenylsulfanyl-phenyl)-thiazole derivatives and theoretical studies of their schiff's base. Phosphorus, Sulfur Silicon Relat Elem. 2003;178(12): 2563-2579.

31. Kalaria P N, Makawana J A, Satasia S P, Raval D K, Zhu H L. Design, synthesis and molecular docking of novel bipyrazolylthiazolone scaffold as a new class of antibacterial agents. *Med Chem Commun*. 2014;5(10):1555-1562.

32. Lykhin A O, Novikova G V, Kuzubov A A, Staloverova N A, Sarmatova N I, Varganov S A, Krasnov P O. A complex of ceftriaxone with Pb (II): synthesis, characterization, and antibacterial activity study. J Coord Chem. 2014;67(16):2783-2794.

33. Gahtori P, Ghosh S K, Singh B, Singh U P, Bhat H R, Ual A. Synthesis, SAR and antibacterial activity of hybrid chloro, dichloro-phenylthiazolyl-s-triazines. Saudi Pharm J. 2012;20(1):35-43.

34. Narayana B, Vijaya R K K, AshalathaB V, Kumari N S. Synthesis of some new 4-(2-chloropyridin-4-yl)-N-aryl-1, 3-thiazol-2-amine derivatives as possible antifungal and antibacterial agents. Phosphorus Sulfur Silicon Relat Elem. 2007;182(1):7-14.

35. Kalhor M, Salehifar M, Nikokar I. Synthesis, characterization, and antibacterial activities of some novel N, N'-disubstitutedthiourea, 2-amino

thiazole, and imidazole-2-thione derivatives. Med Chem Res. 2014;23(6): 2947-2954.

36. Flanagan M E, Brickner S J, Lall M, Casavant J, Deschenes L, Finegan S M, George D M, Granskog K, Hardink J R, Huband M D, Hoang T. Preparation, Gram negative antibacterial activity, and hydrolytic stability of novel siderophore-conjugated monocarbam diols. ACS Med Chem Lett. 2011;2(5):385-390.

37. Lam T, Hilgers M T, Cunningham M L, Kwan B P, Nelson K J, Brown-Driver V, Ong V, Trzoss M, Hough G, Shaw K J, Finn J. Structure-based design of new dihydrofolate reductase antibacterial agents: 7-(benzimidazol-1-yl)-2, 4-diaminoquinazolines. J Med Chem. 2014;57(3):651-668.

# Chapter-4

## Antidiabetic activity of 2-aminothiazoles

Diabetes is a chronic metabolic syndrome categorized by hyperglycemia and cluster of various complications obesity, blurred vision, nephropathy, cataract, neuropathy, dyslipidemia, cardiovascular diseases, lower limb amputation.[1,2] According to IDF around 425 million adults were living with diabetes which will rise to 629 million by 2045. In 2017, more than 1,10,6500 children were living with type 1 diabetes.[3] Albeit various antihyperglycemic drugs have been marketed over the last decade, but most abundantly they show various adverse effects like hypoglycemia, weight gain, peripheral edema.[1,4]

Various compounds containing heterocyclic rings with nitrogen and sulfur have been reported for their potential biological activity.[5] Compounds containing thiazole-2-amines have been reported for having glucokinase activating potential as antidiabetic agentsare following as[6]:

RO0281675
(Hoffman-La-Roche)

LY2121260
(Eli Lilly)

PSN-GK1

Babar et al.(2017) synthesized a series of new ethyl 2-[aryl(thiazol-2-yl) amino] acetates from N-arylthiazole-2-amines and screened its α-glucosidase and β-glucosidase inhibitory activities. Compound **61a** (bearing chloro substituent at position 2 and 4) and compound **61b** displayed excellent inhibitory action towards α-glucosidase and compounds **61c** (bearing bromo substituent at position 4), **61d**, **61e**, **61f** and **61g** displayed the highest inhibitory action towards β-glucosidase.

*Mode of Action*-Compounds **61a**, **61c** and **61h** were found to have inhibition potential towards β-glucosidase and molecular docking study also revealed that compoundsexhibited antidiabetic potential by displaying strong binding interaction with β-glucosidase (PDB: 1CBG).[7]

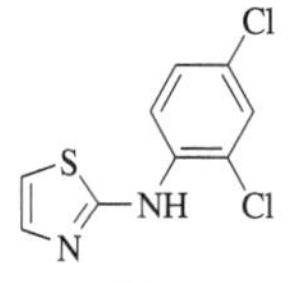

61a 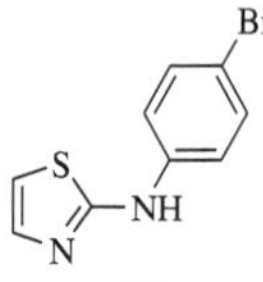    61b 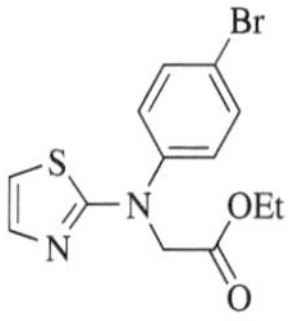    61c 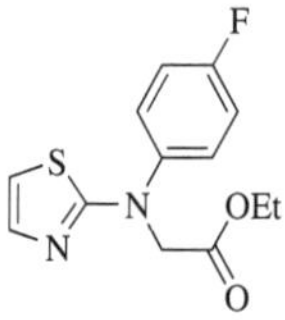    61d

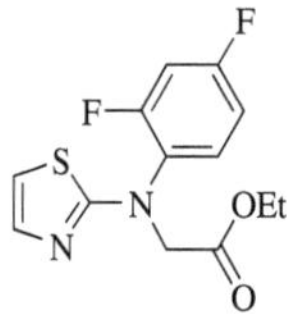

61e 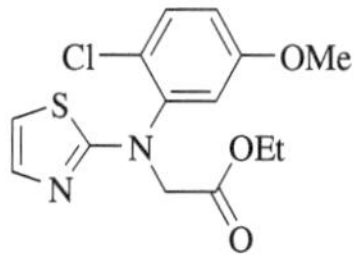    61f 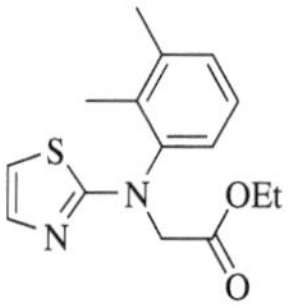    61g 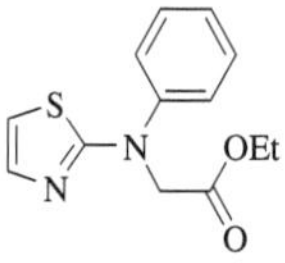    61h

Sravanthi et al. (2017) synthesized a series of 2-(5-(1H-indol-3-yl)-3-phenyl-1Hpyrazol-1-yl)-4-(4-substituted phenyl) thiazole derivatives and screened its α-glucosidase and α-amylase inhibitory activities as antihyperglycaemic agents. Compound 2-(5-(1H-Indol-3-yl)-3-phenyl-1H-pyrazol-1-yl)-4(4-bromo phenyl) thiazole (**62a**) displayed excellent inhibitory potential and compounds such as **62b** and **62c** having fluoro and hydroxyl substituent on phenyl ring of the thiazole moiety also showed remarkable inhibitory activity.

*Mode of Action*-Compounds **62a** showed excellent in vitro antihyperglycemic activity against α-glucosidase and α-amylase and molecular docking study also revealed that compound showed strong binding interaction with α-amylase and α-glucosidase (PDB:1NHZ).[5]

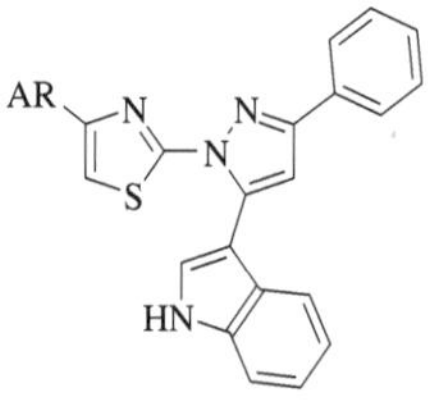

| Comp. | 62a | 62b | 62c |
|-------|-----|-----|-----|
| Ar | 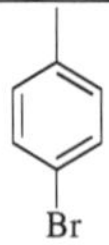 (ring with Br) | 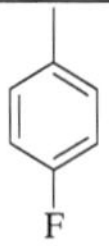 (ring with F) | 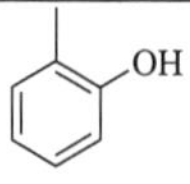 (ring with OH) |

62 (a-c)

Ahmadi et al. (2016) presented new arylidenethiazolidinediones and screened their hypoglycemic and hypolipidemic activity. 5-(4- {2- [(4,6-Di-morpholin-4-yl-[1,3,5] triazin-2-yl)-methyl-amino]-ethoxy}-benzyl)-thiazolidine-2,4-dione **(63)** decreased the blood serum glucose through the both PPAR and ALR2 mechanism and these compounds **63** and 5-{2-chloro-4-[2-(methyl-pyridin-2-yl-amino)-ethoxy]-benzylidene}-thiazolidine-2,4-dione **(64)** enhanced lipid indexes (HDL/LDL and HDL level ratio).

*Mode of Action*-The synthesized compound belongs to a class of insulin sensitizers and reduced the blood serum glucose through PPARγ and aldose reductase (ALR2) inhibition mechanisms.[8]

63

64

N-substituted-5-(furan-2-ylmethylene) thiazolidine-2,4-dione derivatives were synthesized by Mahapatra et al. (2016) and antihyperglycemic activity of these compound increased when thiazolidine-2,4-dione ring bears an alkyl/halo alkyl moiety. (Z)-3-(2-Chloroethyl)-5-(furan-2-ylmethylene) thiazolidine-2,4-dione **(65a)** and (Z)-5-(furan-2ylmethylene)-3-pentylthiazolidine-2,4-dione **(65b)** displayed highest antihyperglycemic activity and significantly reduced blood glucose level in comparison to pioglitazone.

*Mode of Action*-Compounds **65a** and **65b** were found to have potential inhibition against Protein tyrosine phosphatase 1B enzyme that control hyperglycemia andmolecular docking study also revealed that compound showed strong binding interaction with protein tyrosine phosphatase 1B (PDB ID: 2NT7).[9]

| Comp. | 65a | 65b |
|---|---|---|
| R | -CH₂-CH₂-Cl | -CH₂-CH₂-CH₂-CH₂-CH₃ |

$$\text{65 (a-b)}$$

Deshmukh et al. (2017) synthesized a new series of 3-substituted phenyl-2-(4-(tetrazoloquinolin-4-ylmethoxy) phenyl) thiazolidin-4-ones from 2-chloroquinoline-3-carbaldehyde and screened it's in vivo antihyperglycemic activity. Compounds **66 (a-h)** displayed more potent antihyperglycemic activity in comparison to metformin.

*Mode of Action-* Compounds were found to activate peroxisome proliferator receptor γ and diminished the glucose absorption by enhancing the insulin secretion.[1]

| Comp. | R |
|---|---|
| 66a | H |
| 66b | 4-Cl |
| 66c | 4-C₂H₅ |
| 66d | 4-CH₃ |
| 66e | 4-NO₂ |
| 66f | 4-Br |
| 66g | 4-OCH₃ |
| 66h | 2-Cl |

66 (a-h)

Ali et al. (2017) presented hydrazinylarylthiazole based pyridine derivatives and evaluated them for α-glucosidase inhibitory potential. Compound **67a** having dichloro substituents at m, p-position of aryl ring and compound **67b** bearing nitro and hydroxy groups displayed excellent activity. Compound **68a** with dichloro substituent and compound **68b** with nitro and hydroxy groups displayed the highest inhibition against α-glucosidase enzyme. Compounds **68c** and **68d** having dichloro and m-hydroxy analog displayed excellent activity and compound **68e** and **68f** bearing substituent such as m, p-dichloro and m-hydroxy at aryl ring displayed more potent in vitro α-glucosidase inhibitory activity.[10]

67 (a-b)　　　　68 (a-f)

| Comp. | R | Comp. | R |
|---|---|---|---|
| 67a | (2,3,4-trichlorophenyl ring with Cl, Cl) | 68c | (phenyl ring with Cl, Cl) |
| 67b | (phenyl ring with NO$_2$) | 68d | (phenyl ring with OH) |
| 68a | (phenyl ring with Cl, Cl) | 68e | (phenyl ring with Cl, Cl) |
| 68b | (phenyl ring with NO$_2$) | 68f | (phenyl ring with OH) |

Li et al. (2014) presented a new series of urea derivatives which activates both glucokinase (GK) and peroxisome proliferator-activated-γ (PPARγ), it was found that compounds **69a** (having n-pentyl substituent), **69b** (bearing allyl group) and **69c** (with n-pentyl substituent) displayed excellent enzymatic activating activity for peroxisome proliferator-activated-γ (PPARγ) and glucokinase (GK) for treatment of Type 2 diabetes mellitus.

*Modes of Action-* Compounds were found to activate both peroxisome proliferator-activated-γ (PPARγ) and glucokinase (GK). Glucokinase mainly expressed in liver and pancreatic β cell which helped in glycometabolism by promoting insulin secretion and enhanced glycogen synthesis. On another side PPARγ agonist also perform as an insulin sensitizer to improve insulin resistance.[11]

69 (a-c)

| Comp. | R | R$_1$ |
|---|---|---|
| 69a | Ethylene oxide | n-pentyl |
| 69b | Ethylene oxide | Allyl |
| 69c | OH | n-pentyl |

Mao et al. (2012) reported a novel series of thiazole containing benzamide derivatives and investigated for glucokinase (GK) activator ability. Compound **70** was found to be most promising antidiabetic agent with suitable balance of potency and activation profile having $EC_{50}$ value 28.3 nM. The high activity of thiazole derivative 70 was attributed to presence of cyclic secondary amine, which may involve in hydrogen bonding with target site.[12]

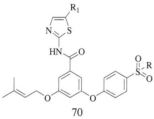

| Comp. | R | R$_1$ |
|-------|---|-------|
| 70 | | F |

70

Navarrete-Vázquezet al. (2014) presented a new series of 2-[2-[(a/b-naphthalen-1-ylsulfonyl) amino]1,3-thiazol-4-yl] acetamide and evaluated for its invitro inhibitory activity towards 11β-hydroxysteroid dehydrogenase type 1. Compounds **71** displayed excellent antidiabetic activity and both compounds bearing peperidine ring in their structure, in which compound **71** showed most potent inhibitory activity regarding Type 2 diabetes mellitus.[13]

| Comp. | R |
|-------|---|
| 71 | Piperidine |

71

Salar et al. (2016) presented a series of 3-thiazolylcoumarin derivatives and evaluated for antidiabetic potential. Compounds displayed α-glucosidase inhibitory potential with $IC_{50}$ value of (0.12 to16.20 µM) in comparison to the reference drug acarbose with $IC_{50}$ 38.25 ± 0.12 µM. It was observed that electron withdrawing centers at one and electron rich centers at the other end of the molecules displayed the more potent inhibitory activity.[14]

| Comp. | R₁ | R₂ |
|---|---|---|
| 72a | | |
| 72b | | |

A novel series of N-(pyrimidin-4-yl) thiazol-2-amine derivatives were synthesized by Song et al. (2011) and evaluated for its antihyperglycemic activity. It was found that compound **73** displayed excellent dual-acting hypoglycemic agent with both Glucokinase (GK) activation and perioxisome proliferator-activated-γ (PPARγ) transcription activities.[15]

| Comp. | R₁ | R₂ | R₃ |
|---|---|---|---|
| 73 | H | CO₂Et | |

73

Ezer et al. (2011) synthesized the morpholino thiazolyl-2,4-thiazolidinediones compounds and evaluated them for glucose uptake and in vitro insulin releasing activity. Compounds **74a**, **75** and **76 (a-f)** at 0.001 mg/ml concentration and compounds **74 (b-f)**, **76 (c-f)** at 0.01 mg/ml concentration were found to stimulate insulin release. Compounds **76e** and **76c** were found as most potent bearing dichloride and phenacyl chloride at N-3 position of TZD ring, respectively.[16]

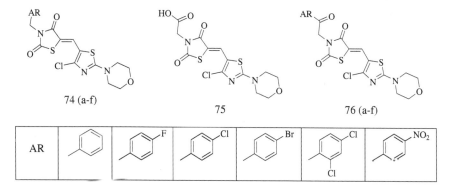

74 (a-f)  75  76 (a-f)

A novel series of 5-fluorophenylpyrazoles and their thioureas, urea derivatives werereported by Faidallah et al. (2016) and evaluated for its antidiabetic activity. Compounds**77a**, **77b**, **78a** and **78b** possess marked hypoglycemic activity and compounds **78a** and **78b** displayed very high lipophilicity in comparison to other compounds.[17]

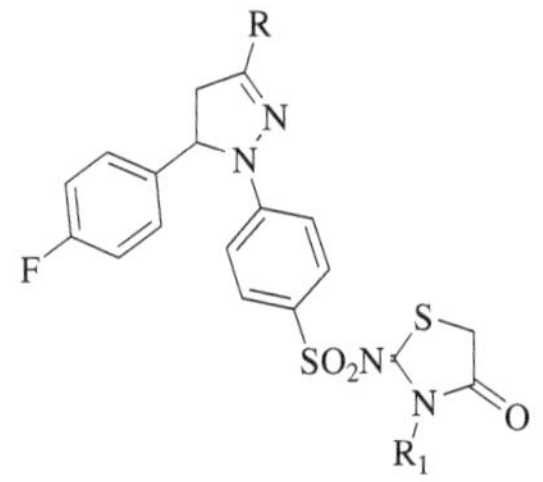

77 (a-b) 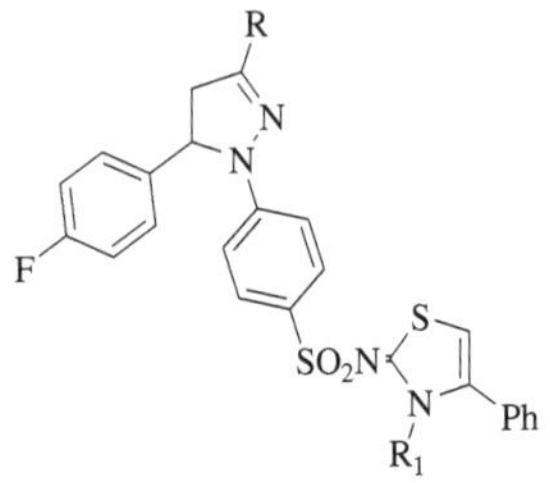          78 (a-b)

| Comp. | R | R$_1$ |
|-------|---|-------|
| 77a | 4-CH$_3$.C$_6$H$_4$ | p-ClC$_6$H$_4$ |
| 77b | 4-CH$_3$.C$_6$H$_4$ | Cyclohexyl |
| 78a | 4-CH$_3$.C$_6$H$_4$ | C$_6$H$_5$ |
| 78b | 4-CH$_3$.C$_6$H$_4$ | p-ClC$_6$H$_4$ |

A new series of isothiazole-based phenylpropanoic acid analogueswere determined by Zhang et al. (2017) and screened them for antidiabetic activity for type 2 diabetes. Compounds **79** having (2-F, 4-Cl) exhibited most potent activity with good EC$_{50}$ values in both β-arrestinand calcium assays. Compound **80a**bearing a methyl group at the 5$^{th}$postion of the isothaizle ring enhanced hGPR120 potency and compound **80b** having Cl group at 3$^{rd}$ position on isothiazole ring exhibited better activity (EC$_{50}$= 56 nM) for hGPR120.[18]

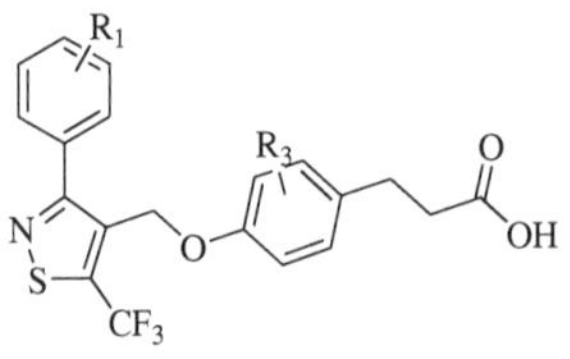

79 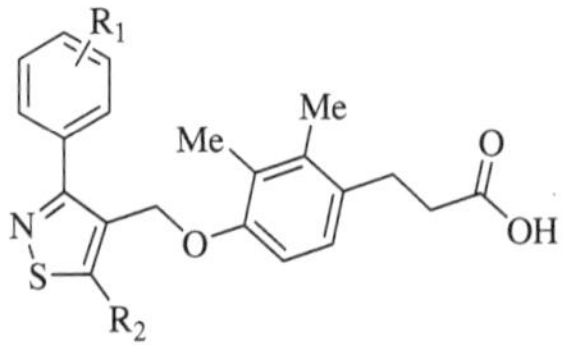          80 (a-b)

| Comp. | $R_1$ | $R_2$ | $R_3$ |
|-------|-------|-------|-------|
| 79 | 2-F, 4-Cl | - | 3,5-di-F |
| 80a | 4-Cl | Me | - |
| 80b | 4-Et | Cl | - |

# References

1. Deshmukh A R, Bhosle M R, Khillare L D, Dhumal S T, Mishra A, Srivastava A K, Mane R A. New tetrazoloquinolinyl methoxyphenyl-4-thiazolidinones: synthesis and antihyperglycemic evaluation. Res Chem Intermediat, 2017;43(2):1107-1120.
2. Ceylan-Unlusoy M, Verspohl E J, Ertan R. Synthesis and antidiabetic activity of some new chromonyl-2, 4-thiazolidinediones. J Enzyme Inhib Med Chem. 2010;25(6):784-789.
3. International Diabetes Federation, diabetes atlas, 8th Edition, 2017
4. Wang Y, Desai M, Ryan P B, DeFalco F J, Schuemie M J, Stang P E, Berlin J A, Yuan Z. Incidence of diabetic ketoacidosis among patients with type 2 diabetes mellitus treated with SGLT2 inhibitors and other antihyperglycemic agents. Diabetes Res Clin Pract. 2017;128:83-90.
5. SravanthiTV, Lulu S S, Vino S, Jayasri M A, Mohanapriya A, Manju S L. Synthesis, docking, and evaluation of novel thiazoles for potent antidiabetic activity. Med Chem Res. 2017;26(6):1306-1315.
6. Matschinsky F M. Assessing the potential of glucokinase activators in diabetes therapy. Nat Rev Drug Discov. 2009;8(5):399.
7. Babar A, Yar M, Tarazi H, Duarte V, Alshammari M B, Gilani M A, IqbalH, Munawwar M A, Alves M J, Khan A F. Molecular docking and glucosidase inhibition studies of novel N-arylthiazole-2-amines and ethyl 2- [aryl (thiazol-2-yl) amino] acetates. Med Chem Res. 2017;26(12):3247-3261.
8. Ahmadi A, Khalili M, Samavat S, Shahbazi E, Nahri-Niknafs B. Synthesis and evaluation of the hypoglycemic and hypolipidemic activity of novel arylidenethiazolidinedione analogson a Type 2 diabetes model. Pharm Chem J. 2016;50(3):165-171.

9. Mahapatra M K, Saini R, Kumar M. Synthesis, anti-hyperglycaemic activity, and in-silico studies of N-substituted 5-(furan-2-ylmethylene) thiazolidine-2, 4-dione derivatives. Res Chem Intermediat. 2016;42(12):8239-8251.

10. Ali F, Khan K M, Salar U, Taha M, Ismail N H, Wadood A, Riaz M, Perveen S. Hydrazinylarylthiazole based pyridine scaffolds: synthesis, structural characterization, in vitro α-glucosidase inhibitory activity, and in silico studies. Eur J Med Chem. 2017;138:255-272.

11. Li Y, Tian K, Qin A, Zhang L, Huo L, Lei L, Shen Z, Song H, Feng Z. Discovery of novel urea derivatives as dual-target hypoglycemic agents that activate glucokinase and ARγ. Eur J Med Chem. 2014;76:182-192.

12. Mao W, Ning M, Liu Z, Zhu Q, Leng Y, Zhang A. Design, synthesis, and pharmacological evaluation of benzamide derivatives as glucokinase activators. Bioorg Med Chem. 2012;20(9):2982-2991.

13. Navarrete-Vázquez G, Morales-Vilchis M G, Estrada-Soto S, Ramírez-Espinosa J J, Hidalgo-Figueroa S, Nava-Zuazo C, Tlahuext H, Leon-Rivera I, Medina-Franco J L, Lopez-Vallejo F, Webster S P. Synthesis of 2-{2-[(α/β-naphthalen-1-ylsulfonyl) amino]-1, 3-thiazol-4-yl} acetamides with 11β-hydroxysteroid dehydrogenase inhibition and in combo antidiabetic activities. Eur J Med Chem. 2014;74:179-186.

14. Salar U, Taha M, Khan K M, Ismail N H, Imran S, Perveen S, Gul S, Wadood A. Syntheses of new 3-thiazolyl coumarin derivatives, in vitro α-glucosidase inhibitory activity, and molecular modeling studies. Eur J Med Chem. 2016;122:196-204.

15. Song H P, Tian K, Lei L, Shen Z F, Liu S X, Zhang L J, Song H R, Jin X F, Feng Z Q. Novel N-(pyrimidin-4-yl) thiazol-2-amine derivatives as dual-action hypoglycemic agents that activate GK and ARγ. Acta Pharm Sin B. 2011;1(3):166-171.

16. Ezer M, Yıldırım L T, Bayro O, Verspohl E J, Dundar O B. Synthesis and antidiabetic activity of morpholinothiazolyl-2, 4-thiazolidindione derivatives. J Enzyme Inhib Med Chem. 2012;27(3): 419-427.

17. Faidallah H M, Al-Mohammadi M M, AlamryK A, Khan K A. Synthesis and biological evaluation of fluoropyrazolesulfonylurea and thiourea derivatives as possible antidiabetic agents. J Enzyme Inhib Med Chem. 2016;31(supl):157-163.

18. Zhang X, Cai C, Sui Z, Macielag M, Wang Y, Yan W, Suckow A, Hua H, Bell A, Haug P, Claer W. Discovery of an isothiazole-based phenylpropanoic acid GPR120 agonist as a development candidate for Type 2 diabetes. ACS Med Chem Lett. 2017;8(9):947-952.

# Chapter-5

## Antimycobacterial activity of 2-aminothiazoles

Tuberculosis is an extremely contagious and airborne disease instigated by Mycobacterium tuberculosis.[1] According to World Health Organization Global tuberculosis report 2017, TB is one of top 10 causal agents which is responsible for death worldwide. In 2016, around 1.7 million people died from the disease and in low and middle income countries 95 % death been acted from TB. In cases of children 2,50,000 children died from TB. Even though 40 % of HIV deaths were due to TB so we can say that TB is leading killer of HIV-positive people.[2] Multidrug-resistant tuberculosis is a form of TB in which bacteria do not respond to two more potent drugs, isoniazid and rifampicin (first-line anti-TB drugs) whereas Extensively drug-resistant TB (XDR-TB) is a more severe form of MDR-TB in which bacteria do not respond to the most efficacious second-line anti-TB drugs (amikacin, kanamycin or capreomycin)[3],so patients have to live without any treatment options. In 2016, it was estimated that nearby 600,000 new cases with resistance to rifampicin (most effective first-line drug) were there while 6.2% of MDR-TB were estimated to have XDR-tuberculosis.[2]

Among the promising molecules, 2-aminothiazoles having target specificity and potent inhibitor of MTB are of particular interest. 2-Aminothiazoles scaffold is basically similar to thiolactomycin, which is challenging antibiotic and inhibits KasA (β- ketoacyl-ACP synthase) in mtFabH fatty acid synthesis and therefore inhibiting cell wall synthesis leading to cell death.[1,4] Nitazoxanide, and its active metabolite are well known for their inhibitory activity against replicative and non-replicative Mtb.[5]

| Nitazoxanide | Tizoxanide |

A new series of isopropylthiazole derivatives triazolothiadiazines, azolothiadiazoles, thioxotriazoles, triazolothiadiazole, arylideneaminotriazoloethiones and oxadiazoloethiones were synthesized by Suresh et al. and screened for antitubercular activity towards *Mycobacterium tuberculosis H37Rv*. Compounds such as **81a** and **81b** demonstrated the most potent antitubercular potential (MIC 4 and 8μg/ml) towards *M. tuberculosis H37Rv*. The compounds **81c** bearing p-methoxy and **81d** having p-dimethyl amino substituent displayed reasonable anti-tubercular activity at MIC 8-31.25 μg/ml.[6]

| Comp. | X | R |
|-------|-----|-----------|
| 81a | N-CH$_3$ | 4-N(CH$_3$)$_2$ |
| 81b | N-CH$_3$ | 3,4,5-OCH$_3$ |
| 81c | N-CH$_3$ | 4-OCH$_3$ |
| 81d | O | 4-N(CH$_3$)$_2$ |

81 (a-d)

Azzali et al. (2017) synthesized a series of substituted 2-aminothiazoles and investigated for their inhibitory activity towards the growth of actively nonreplicating persistent, replicating and resistant *M. tuberculosis* strains. It was observed that compounds N-phenyl-5-(2-(p-tolylamino) thiazol-4-yl) isoxazole-3-carboxamide (MIC 0.125−0.25 μg/ml) and N-(pyridin-2-yl)5-(2-(p-tolylamino) thiazol-4-yl) isoxazole-3-carboxamide (MIC 0.06−0.125 μg/ml) exhibited excellent inhibitory activity against *M. tuberculosis* strains.[7]

| Comp. | R$_1$ | R$_2$ | R$_3$ | X |
|-------|-------|-------|-------|---|
| 82a | 4-CH$_3$ | | H | C |
| 82b | 4-CH$_3$ | | H | C |

82 (a-b)

A novel series of 4,4'-(4,6-dimethoxy-1,3-phenylene)-bis-(N-substituted thiazol-2-amine) analogues were reported by Baba et al. (2017) and evaluated for antitubercular activity towards *M. tuberculosis H37Rv* andantibacterial activities against *B. subtilis* and *E. coli* strains. Compounds **83a**, **83b** and **83c** displayed excellent antitubercular activity.

| Comp. | R |
|-------|---|
| 83a | (3-chloro-4-fluorophenyl group) |
| 83b | (4-morpholinophenyl group) |
| 83c | (2,6-dimethylpyridinyl group) |

(Structure of 83 (a-c): MeO and OMe substituted benzene with two thiazole rings, R-NH and HN-R)

A series of styryl hydrazine thiazole hybrids derived from dehydrozingerone (DZG) scaffold reported by Hampannavar et al. (2016) and studied for antimycobacterial activity towards *M. tuberculosis H37Rv*. The results of antimycobacterial evaluation showed that compound **84a** (MIC = 1.5 µM) having p-amino group on phenyl ring at 4$^{th}$ position of the thiazole moiety displayed more potent antimycobacterial activity and compounds **84b** (MIC = 15 µM) bearing with methoxyl (OCH$_3$) group on thiazolyl phenyl ring acclaimed better inhibitory activity.[9]

(Structure of 84 (a-b): H$_3$CO and H$_3$CO substituted benzene with CH$_3$, H, N-N, thiazole, and R)

| Comp. | R |
|-------|---|
| 84a | -NH$_2$ |
| 84b | OCH$_3$ |

84 (a-b)

Aridoss et al. (2009) synthesized thiazole and thiazolidinone derivatives via stereospecific synthesis and evaluated them for their antimycobacterial potential towards *M. tuberculosis*. Compounds **85 (a-c)** and **86 (a-c)** demonstrated twofold superior potency (MIC= 16µg/ml) than reference drug Rifampicin with MIC 32µg/mL. It was inferred that replacement of methyl group with ethyl in C-3 piperidone group totally reduced the antimycobacterial potential while halogen attachment (viz. F, Cl and Br) and methoxy group to nitrogen of piperdine moiety and Schiff bases enhanced antimycobacterial activity.[10]

85 (a-c)                    86 (a-c)

| Comp. | R$_1$ | R$_2$ | Comp. | R$_1$ | R$_2$ |
|-------|-------|-------|-------|-------|-------|
| 85a | H | Cl | 86a | H | F |
| 85b | H | Br | 86b | H | Och3 |
| 85c | CH$_3$ | H | 86c | CH$_3$ | H |

Bellale et al. (2014) reported a series of diarylthiazole derivatives and evaluated for its antitubercular activity towards *M. tuberculosis* by targeting PrrB-PrrA. PrrBA system plays a significant role in pathogenicity and metabolic adaptation to stress and has a vital, conserved regulatory mechanism in *M. tuberculosis*. Compound **87** displayed maximum potential with MIC=0.12μM.[11]

87

Makam et al. (2013) reported a series of 2-(2-hydrazinyl) thiazole derivatives with various substitution at 2-, 4- and 5- position and investigated for their inhibitory activity towards *M. tuberculosis* H37Rv. Compounds such as ethyl-4-methyl-2-[(E)-2-[1-(pyridin-2yl) ethylidene] hydrazin-1-yl]-1,3-thiazole-5-carboxylate **(88a)** and ethyl-2-[(E)-2-[(2hydroxyphenyl) methylidene] hydrazin-1-yl]-4-methyl-1,3-thiazole-5-carboxylate **(88b)**displayed appreciable activity.

*Mode of Action*-Compound **88a** and **88b** were found to have inhibition potential against β – ketoacyl – ACP synthase (KasA) in mtFabH fatty acid synthesis which is responsible for inhibition of cell wall biosynthesis that leads to the death of Mtb. Molecular docking study also revealed that compound showed strong binding interaction with β-ketoacyl-ACP synthase protein (PDB:2WGD).[1]

88a

88b

A series of aminothiazole analogues was reported by Meissner et al. (2013) based on a hit from whole-cell screening towards *M. tuberculosis*. It was observed that compounds such as **89a** (MIC=0.19-0.39 μM), **89b** (MIC=0.049-0.78μM), **89c** and **89d** (MIC=0.024 μM or 0.008 μg/ml) bearing (phenyl, 3-benzyloxyphenyl, 3-bromophenyl, 3-chlorophenyl) displayed high antitubercular activity.[12]

89 (a-d)

| Comp. | R |
|---|---|
| 89a | Phenyl |
| 89b | 3-Benzyloxyphenyl |
| 89c | 3-Bromophenyl |
| 89d | 3-Chlorophenyl |

A novel series of 1-(4-(-2-substitutedthiazol-4-yl) phenethyl-4-(3-(4-substitutedpiperazin-1-yl) alkyl) piperazine derivatives was reported by Nagesh et al. (2014) and evaluated for antitubercular activity towards *M. tuberculosis H37Rv*. The evaluation study indicated compound **90a** (MIC=1.56μg/ml) has the maximum inhibitory potential and compounds such as **90b**, **90c** and **90d** showed reasonable activity (MIC=6.25μg/ml) and compounds **90e**, **90f**, **90g**, **90h** and **90i** displayed excellent inhibitory activity (MIC=3125μg/ml) towards *M. tuberculosis*.[5]

90 (a-i)

| Comp. | R | $R_1$ | n | Comp. | R | $R_1$ | n |
|---|---|---|---|---|---|---|---|
| 90a | NHCH$_3$ | (PH)$_2$CH | 3 | 90f | NH$_2$ | (PH)$_2$CH | 3 |
| 90b | CH$_3$ | (PH)$_2$CH | 3 | 90g | NH$_2$ | (PH)$_2$CH | 4 |
| 90c | NH$_2$ | 4-NO$_2$PH | 3 | 90h | NHCH$_3$ | 2-ClPH | 4 |
| 90d | NH$_2$ | 4-NO$_2$PH | 5 | 90i | NH$_2$ | 2-Py | 3 |
| 90e | NH$_2$ | PH | 3 | | | | |

Pieroni et al. (2013) presented a series of N-substituted 2-amino thiazole derivatives and investigated their antitubercular activity. Selected compounds such as **91a** and **91b** exhibited the highly activation against nonreplicating persistent phenotype (NRB-TB) as well as also active against replicating mycobacterial strain. SAR study stated that the scaffold of 2-aminothiazole gave a various valuable hints for the additional analogs design such as the amino group and the lipophilic functional group like as chlorine at 4th position of the 2-aminothiazole gave better activity. On the other side the polar group like methoxy seems to be essential in order to maintain antitubercular potential.[3]

| Comp. | R₁ | R₂ | R₃ | R₄ |
|-------|----------|----|----|-------|
| 91a | 2-F,5-CF₃ | H | H | 4-Cl |
| 91b | 4-OCH₃ | H | H | 4-CH₃ |

91 (a-b)

Samala et al. (2014) synthesized a novel series of 3 and 5 substituted 2-iminothiazolidine-4-ones and evaluated for anti-TBactivity towards *M. tuberculosis*. Compounds 2-imino-3-(5-nitrothiazol-2-yl)-5-(3,4,5trimethoxy-benzylidene) thiazolidin-4-one (**92a**) exhibited more potent in vitro activity with MIC of 3.31µM. The compounds containing4-methoxyl (**92b**, **93a**, **94a**), 4-benzyloxy (**92c**, **93b**, **94b**) and 4-hydroxyl (**92d**, **93c**, **94c**) substituent at C-5 position displayed excellent antitubercular activity.[13]

92 (a-d)

93 (a-c)

94 (a-c)

| Comp. | R₁ | Comp. | R₁ | Comp. | R₁ |
|-------|-----------------------|-------|------------------|-------|------------------|
| 92a | 3,4,5-trimethoxyphenyl | 93a | 4-methoxyphenyl | 94a | 4-methoxyphenyl |
| 92b | 4-methoxyphenyl | 93b | 4-benzyloxyphenyl | 94b | 4-benzyloxyphenyl |
| 92c | 4-benzyloxyphenyl | 93c | 4-hydroxylphenyl | 94c | 4-hydroxylphenyl |
| 92d | 4-hydroxylphenyl | | | | |

Surineni et al. (2016) synthesized a novel series of dibenzofuran tethered thiazolyl 1,2,3-triazolesand and screened for antitubercular activity towards *M. tuberculosis H37Rv*. Compounds **95a** (MIC=1.56 μg/mL), **95b** and **96** with (MIC= 3.13μg/mL) displayed highest in vitro antimycobacterial activity.[4]

95 (a-b)                                    96

| Comp. | R |
|-------|-----|
| 95a | ⌇⌇⌇⌇ |
| 95b | n-$C_{12}H_{25}$ |
| 96 | H |

Zitko et al. (2018) reported a series of hybrid molecules combining first line antitubercular drug pyrazinamide (PZA) with 4-phenylthaizol-2-amine scaffold and investigated their inhibitory activity towards *M. avium, M. tuberculosis H37Rv, M. smegmatis* and *M. kansasii*at neutral pH in a microplate Alamar Blue Assay. Compound 6-chloro-N-[4-(4fluorophenyl) thiazol-2yl] pyrazine-2-carboxamide (**97a**) displayed highest inhibitory activity towards *M. avium, M. tuberculosis* and *M. kansasii* with MIC 0.78 μg/mL (2.3 μM) and other compounds such as **97b**, **97c**, and **97d** also depicted appreciable activity.

*Mode of Action*-Compound were found to have inhibition potential against β-ketoacyl-(acyl-carrierprotein) synthase III (FabH or KAS III) which is responsible for the synthesis of fatty acid that causes alteration in cell wall biosynthesis and leads to death of *M. tuberculosis*. Molecular docking study also revealed that compound showed strong binding interaction with mycobacterial FabH similar to *E. coli* FabH (PDB: 3IL9).[14]

97 (a-d)

| Comp. | $R_1$ | X | $R_2$ |
|-------|-------|-----|-------|
| 97a | 4-F | CH | 6-Cl |
| 97b | 4-F | CH | 5-Cl |
| 97c | 4-OCH$_3$ | CH | 5-Cl |
| 97d | 4-OCH$_3$ | CH | 6-Cl |

# References

1. Makam P, Kankanala R, Prakash A, Kannan T. 2-(2-Hydrazinyl) thiazole derivatives: Design, synthesis and in vitro antimycobacterial studies. Eur J Med Chem. 2013;69:564-576.
2. World Health Organization. Global tuberculosis report 2017.
3. Pieroni M, Wan B, Cho S, Franzblau S G, Costantino G. Design, synthesis and investigation on the structure–activity relationships of N-substituted 2-aminothiazole derivatives as antitubercular agents. Eur J Med Chem. 2014;72:26-34.
4. Surineni G, Yogeeswari P, Sriram D, Kantevari S. Click-based synthesis and antitubercular evaluation of dibenzofuran tethered thiazolyl-1, 2, 3-triazolyl acetamides. Bioorg MedChem Lett. 2016;26(15): 3684-3689.
5. Nagesh H N, Suresh A, Sairam S D S S, Sriram D, Yogeeswari P, Sekhar K V G C. Design, synthesis and antimycobacterial evaluation of 1-(4-(2-substitutedthiazol-4-yl) phenethyl)-4-(3-(4-substitutedpiperazin-1-yl) alkyl) piperazine hybrid analogues. Eur J Med Chem. 2014;84: 605-613.
6. Kumar G S, Rajendraprasad Y, Mallikarjuna B P, Chandrashekar S M, Kistayya C. Synthesis of some novel 2-substituted-5-[isopropylthiazole] clubbed 1, 2, 4-triazole and 1, 3, 4-oxadiazoles as potential antimicrobial and antitubercular agents. Eur J Med Chem, 2010;45(5):2063-2074.
7. Azzali E, Machado D, Kaushik A, Vacondio F, Flisi S, Cabassi C S, Lamichhane G, Viveiros M, Costantino G, Pieroni M. Substituted N-phenyl-5-(2-(phenylamino) thiazol-4-yl) isoxazole-3-carboxamides are valuable antitubercular candidates that evade innate efflux machinery. J Med Chem, 2017;60(16):7108-7122.
8. Baba N K, Ashok D, Rao B A, Sarasija M, Murthy N Y S, Srinivasarao V, Parthasarathy T. Microwave-assisted synthesis of bis (N-substituted thiazol-2-amine) derivatives and their biological activities. Heterocycl Commun. 2017;23(5): 405-409.
9. Hampannavar G A, Karpoormath R, Palkar M B, Shaikh M S, Chandrasekaran B. Dehydrozingerone inspired styryl hydrazine thiazole hybrids as promising class of antimycobacterial agents. ACS Med Chem Lett. 2016;7(7):686-691.

10. Aridoss G, Amirthaganesan S, Kim M S, Kim J T, Jeong Y T. Synthesis, spectral and biological evaluation of some new thiazolidinones and thiazoles based on t-3-alkyl-r-2, c-6-diarylpiperidin-4-ones. Eur J Med Chem. 2009;44(10): 4199-4210.

11. Bellale E, Naik M, Ambady A, Narayan A, Ravishankar S, Ramachandran V, Kaur P, McLaughlin R, Whiteaker J, Morayya S, Guptha S. Diarylthiazole: an antimycobacterial scaffold potentially targeting PrrB-PrrA two-component system. J Med Chem. 2014;57(15): 6572-6582.

12. Meissner A, Boshoff H I, Vasan M, Duckworth B P, Barry III C E, Aldrich C C. Structure–activity relationships of 2-aminothiazoles effective against Mycobacterium tuberculosis. Bioorg Med Chem. 2013;21(21):6385-6397.

13. Samala G, Madhuri C, Sridevi J P, Nallangi R, Perumal Y, Dharmarajan S. Synthesis and antitubercular evaluation of 2-iminothiazolidine-4-ones. Eur J Chem. 2014;5(3), 550-556.

14. Zitko J, Jand'ourek O, Paterova P, Navratilova L, Kunes J, Vinsova J, Dolezal M. Design, synthesis and antimycobacterial activity of hybrid molecules combining pyrazinamide with a 4-phenylthiazol-2-amine scaffold. Med Chem Commun. 2018;9(4):685-696.

# Chapter-6

## Anti-inflammatory activity of 2-aminothiazoles

Inflammation is a physiological reaction which causes redness, swelling, hot, and often painful, especially as a reaction to injury or infection on body parts and it is associated with many chronic diseases, including atherosclerosis, allergy, arthritis and auto-immune diseases. The cyclooxygenase (COX) enzyme which converts the arachidonic acid to Prostaglandin G2 and the peroxidase activity responsible for the conviction of PGG2 to Prostaglandin H2 (PGH2) which is responsible for the inflammation[1] and various diseases and conditions which include chronic inflammation are like asthma, ulcerative colitis, rheumatoid arthritis etc. Rheumatoid arthritis influences approximately 1% of population and it affects women more than men between the ages of 40 to 70 years.[2] Inflammatory bowel disease incidences are also rising in developing countries and increasingly considered an emerging worldwide disease.[3] Nonsteroidal anti-inflammatory drugs (NSAIDs), like aceclofenac, ibuprofen and ketoprofen are used to cure of inflammatory disorders.[4] 2-Aminothiazole containing drugs which are used to treat inflammatory disorders are like fanetizole, meloxicam and Sudoxicam.[5]

Fanetizole    Meloxicam

Sudoxicam

A new series of diphenylthiazole analogues were presented by Abdelazeem et al. (2015) and screened for its anti-inflammatory activity. Compound **98a** exhibited highest inhibitory activity on inflamed animal paws. Compounds of urea based structure bearing cyclic and bicyclic hydrophobic aliphatic side chain i.e., **98b** and **98c** with aliphatic side chain, e.g., **98d** and **98e** displayed admirable anti-inflammatory properties. The compounds of amide analogs with large hydrophobic chain, i.e., **99a** and **99b** increased anti-inflammatory properties because hydrophobic character enhanced the potency to penetrate different physiological membranes and help them to arrive inflammatory sites more efficiently.

*Mode of Action*-Compound **98e** was found to have inhibition potential against cyclooxygenase-1 (COX-1) enzyme. Molecular docking study also revealed that compound showed strong binding interaction with COX-1(PDB: 3KK6).[4]

98 (a-e)                99 (a-b)

| Comp. | R | Comp. | R |
|---|---|---|---|
| 98a | HN—(benzothiazole) | 98e | ⸳N-H⸳ (butyl chain) |
| 98b | HN—(adamantyl) | 99a | ⸳N-H⸳ (butyl chain) |
| 98c | HN—(cyclohexyl) | 99b | (naphthyl)-N-H...H-N⸳ |
| 98d | ⸳N-H⸳ (butyl chain) | | |

Iyer et al. (2017) reported a series of 1,3,4-oxadiazole and investigated for anti-inflammatory and antioxidant activity. The compounds bearing aryl substitution at second position of the 1,3,4-oxadiazole moiety displayed excellent edema inhibition, in which compound **100a** having pyridin-3-yl substitution exhibited the highest edema inhibition of 82.27% and on the other side compounds such as **100b**, **100c** and **100d** depicted better antioxidant activity.

*Mode of Action*-Compounds **100d** and **100e** showed the highest inhibition potential against cyclooxygenase-2 (COX-2) and cyclooxygenase-1 (COX-1) enzyme. Molecular docking study also explained that compound displayed greater binding interaction with COX-1 enzyme (PDB: 1CQE) and COX-2 enzyme (PDB: 3LN1).[1]

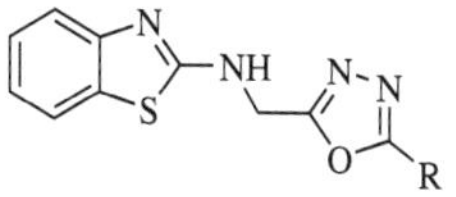

100 (a-e)

| Comp. | R |
|-------|---|
| 100a | 3-$C_5H_4N$ |
| 100b | 2-$NH_2C_6H_4$ |
| 100c | 4-$NH_2C_6H_4$ |
| 100d | 4-$OHC_6H_4$ |
| 100e | 3,5-$(NO_2)_2C_6H_3$ |

A novel series of 2-imino-4-thiazolidinone derivatives reported by Ali et al. (2016) and evaluated for its anti-inflammatory towards TNF-α target. The synthesized compounds were investigated by in vitro, in vivo and in silico studies, and compounds exhibited better anti-inflammatory activity especially compounds **101a** and **101b** displayed excellent inhibition of TNF-α.[6]

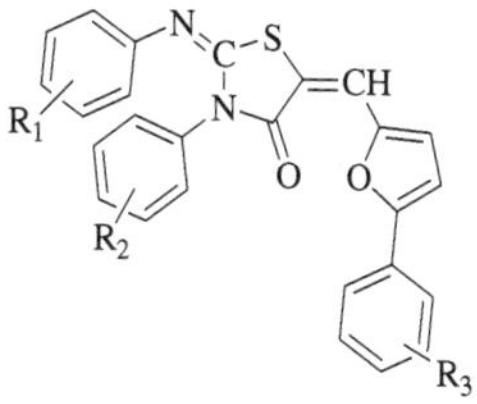

101 (a-b)

| Comp. | $R_1$ | $R_2$ | $R_3$ |
|-------|-------|-------|-------|
| 101a | p-$OCH_3$ | p-$OC_2H_5$ | o-Cl |
| 101b | p-$OCH_3$ | o-$OCH_3$ | o-Cl |

Lin et al. (2004) recognized two new compounds **102a** and **102b** which displayed anti-inflammatory activity in a mouse model of albumin-induced allergy/asthma by reducing the lung inflammation.

*Mode of Action*-Compound exhibited the potent inhibition of T-cell activation which developed immunosuppressive agent to cure inflammation and autoimmune disorder also diminished calcium mobilization, PLCγ1 tyrosine phosphorylation and IL-2 secretion.[7]

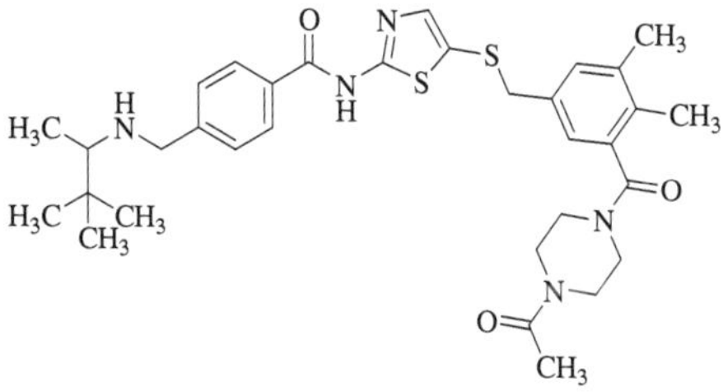

102a

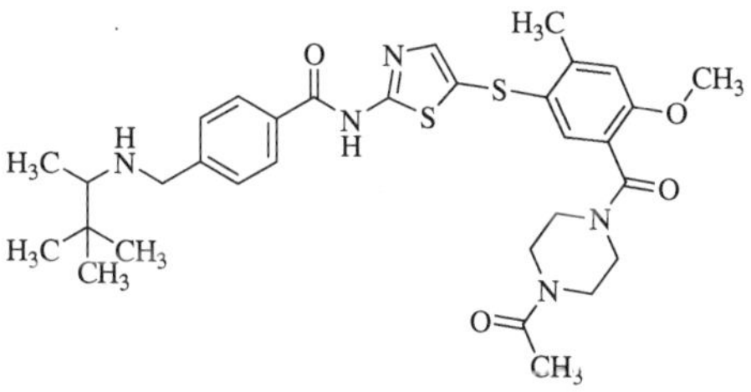

102b

Ge et al. (2017) designed some new thiazole derivatives towards acute lung injury (ALI) which is an inflammatory syndrome of airway initiated by failure of the respiratory system. From the synthesized compounds, compound **103** was found to have excellent inhibition potential towards pro-inflammatory enzyme.

*Mode of Action*-Compound displayed the anti-inflammatory activity by inhibiting the both cyclooxygenase-2 (COX-2) and Prostaglandin E2 (PGE2)enzyme.[8] ·

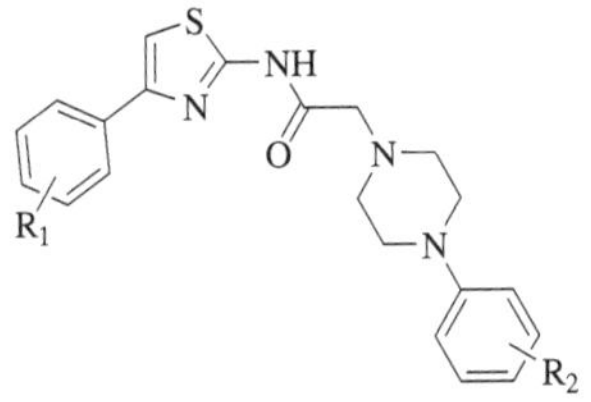

| Comp. | R₁ | R₂ |
|-------|-----|-----|
| 103 | 4-F | H |

103

Helal et al. (2013) synthesized a new series of thiazole compounds and evaluated for its anti-inflammatory and antibacterial activity. Compounds such as **104a, 104b, 105a** and **105b** displayed the anti-inflammatory activity with % inhibition ranges from 35% to 87%, in which compound **104a** and **104b** exhibited the highest inhibition percent range from 85-87% and displayed excellent inhibitory activity towards *S. aureus and B. cereus.*[9]

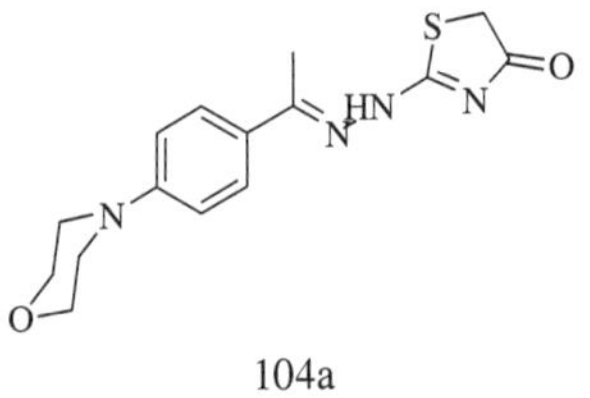

104a

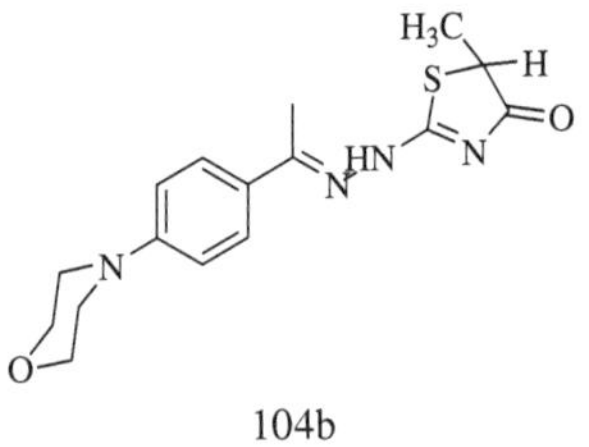

104b

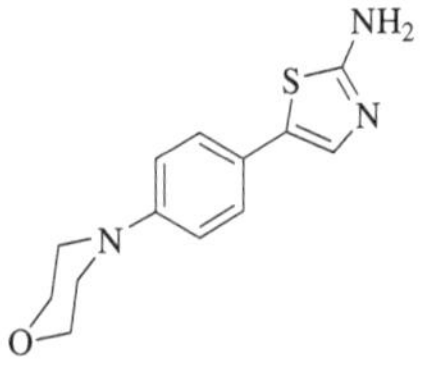

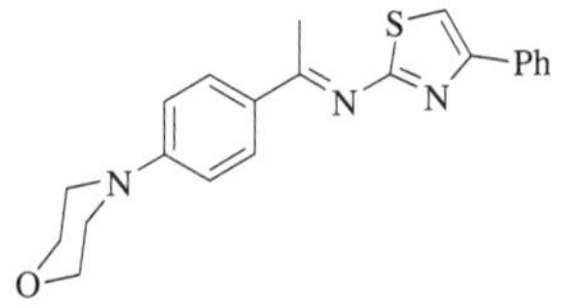

105a

105b

A new series of 4-phenyl-5-pyridyl-1,3-thiazole was synthesized by Miwatashi et al. (2005) and screened for its inhibitory action on p38 mitogen-activated protein kinase and pro-inflammatory cytokine TNF-α. Compound **106a** displayed the highest inhibitory activity against rheumatoid arthritis by p38 MAP kinase inhibitor at $IC_{50}$=7.1. The substitution of an amino group (**106b, 106c, 106d** and **106e**) enhanced the activity in comparison to methyl group on pyridine ring.[10]

| Comp. | $R_1$ | $R_2$ | $R_3$ |
|-------|-------|-------|-------|
| 106a | PhCONH | 3-Me | Et |
| 106b | $NH_2$ | 3-Me | Et |
| 106c | $PhCH_2NH$ | 3-Me | Et |
| 106d | $Ph(CH_2)_2NH$ | 3-Me | Et |
| 106e | $Ph(CH_2)_3NH$ | 3-Me | Et |

106 (a-e)

Kim et al. (2014) synthesized N-adamantyl-4-methylthiazol-2-amines and investigated for their potential towards lipopolysaccharide (LPS)-induced inflammation. Compound **107** displayed the anti-inflammatory activity by inhibiting tumor necrosis factor-a (TNF-a), nitric oxide, interleukin-1b (IL-1B) and reactive oxygen species in culture BV-2 microglial cell. Compound **107** also diminished the cyclooxygenase-2expression, inducible nitric oxide synthase (iNOS) and NADPH oxidase (NOX).[11]

107

A new series of N-(4-aryl-1,3-thiazol-2-yl)-2-(2,4-dioxo-1,3-thiazolidin-5-yl) acetamides and N-(1,3-benzothiazol-2-yl)-2-(2,4-dioxo-1,3-thiazolidin-5-yl)acetamide derivatives reported by Koppireddi et al. (2013) and investigated for anti-inflammatory activity. Compounds **108a, 108b, 109a** and **109b** exhibited the highest anti-inflammatory activity whereas compounds **108c** and **108d** showed the highest anti-oxidant activity. Compounds **108c** and **109 (a-b)** exhibited both anti-inflammatory and anti-oxidant activities.[12]

| Comp. | R |
|-------|---|
| 108a | H |
| 108b | 0-Me |
| 108c | o-OMe |
| 108d | m-Me |
| 109a | 6-NO$_2$ |
| 109b | 6-OMe |

108 (a-d)          109 (a-b)

A new series of adamantanyl analogues was reported by Kouatly et al. (2017) and investigated for its anti-inflammatory activity. As per docking analysis, it was found that compounds **110a, 110b, 110c, 110d, 110e** and **110f** exhibited the highest anti-inflammatory potential. Compound **110d** (having NO$_2$ substitution) and compound **110c** bearing (Cl substitution) on phenyl ring exhibited excellent anti-inflammatory with an IC$_{50}$ value of 25µM and 39µM.

*Mode of Action*-Compound displayed the anti-inflammatory activity by inhibiting cyclooxygenase-1 (COX-1) and lipoxygenase (LOX) enzyme. Molecular docking study also explained that compound displayed greater binding interaction with COX-1 enzyme (PDB:1EQH) and LOX enzyme (PDB: 3O8Y).[13]

110 (a-f)

| Comp. | R | X |
|-------|---|---|
| 110a | 4-Cl | adamantanyl |
| 110b | 3-Cl | adamantanyl |
| 110c | 2-Cl | adamantanyl |
| 110d | 2-NO$_2$ | adamantanyl |
| 110e | 4-OH | adamantanyl |
| 110f | 4-OH-3-OCH$_3$ | adamantanyl |

A series of 3-(2-amino-4-thiazolyl) coumarin derivatives reported by Ramagiri et al. (2015) and screened for its anti-inflammatory and anti-oxidant activity. Compound **111a** displayed excellent anti-inflammatory activity at 150µg/ml with 93% inhibition and other compounds such as **111b, 111c, 111d,111e, 111f** and **111g** displayed the valuable anti-inflammatory as well as anti-oxidant activity.[14]

111 (a-g)

| Comp. | R | R$_1$ | R$_2$ | R$_3$ |
|-------|---|-------|-------|-------|
| 111a | OCH$_3$ | H | p-Tolyl | H |
| 111b | H | H | p-Tolyl | H |
| 111c | 5,6 benzo | 5,6 benzo | p-Tolyl | H |
| 111d | H | H | p-Anisyl | H |
| 111e | OCH$_3$ | H | p-Anisyl | H |
| 111f | H | Br | p-Anisyl | H |
| 111g | H | H | p-Chlorophenyl | H |

Sharma et al. (2009) presented a new series of 4-benzyl-1,3-thiazole derivatives and investigated for anti-inflammatory activity. Compounds such as **112a** (having p-OCH$_3$) and **112b** (with p-Cl) and **112c** (with OCH$_3$ group) and **112d** (with p-Cl) displayed most potent anti-inflammatory activity.

*Mode of Action*-Compound was found to have inhibition potential against PGF2-alpha (COX pathway) and LTB4 (LOX pathway) and showed excellent anti-inflammatory activity.[15]

112 (a-d)

| Comp. | R$_1$ | R$_2$ |
|-------|-------|-------|
| 112a | | OCH$_3$ |
| 112b | | Cl |
| 112c | | OCH$_3$ |
| 112d | | Cl |

A novel series of benzo[d]thiazole-hydrazones derivatives were reported by Wang et al. (2017) and investigated for in vitro anti-inflammatory activity. SAR study demonstrated that electron-donating groups (OH and OCH$_3$) recommended inhibitory activity towards H$^+$/K$^+$ ATPase, and electron-withdrawing groups (Cl, F, NO$_2$ and Br) recommended anti-inflammatory activity. Compounds **113a**, **113b**, **113c** and **113d** showed highest anti-inflammatory activity and compounds **113e**, **113f**, **113g**, and **113h** diplayed valuable inhibitory activity towards H$^+$/K$^+$ ATPase. *Mode of Action*-Compounds **113c**, **113e** and **113f** were found to have potential inhibition against cyclooxygenase-2 (COX-2) and H$^+$/K$^+$ ATPase. Molecular docking study also explained that compound displayed strong binding interaction with COX-2 enzyme (PDB: 1PXX) and H$^+$/K$^+$ ATPase (PDB ID:2ZXE).[16]

113 (a-h)

| Comp. | R | Comp. | R |
|-------|---|-------|---|
| 113a | Cl | 113e | OCH$_3$ / OCH$_3$ / OCH$_3$ |
| 113b | Br | 113f | OH / OH / OH |

| 113c | $O_2N$ —⟨⟩— $NO_2$ | 113g | (thiophene ring) |
|------|---------------------|------|------------------|
| 113d | $Br$ —⟨⟩— $Br$ | 113h | (indole ring, NH) |

A series of sulfone-substituted 2,4,5-triarylthiazoles was synthesized by Carter et al. (1999) and investigated for their anti-inflammatory potential via carrageenan paw edema method. It was observed that compound **114** having chlorine, fluorineand methane sulfonyl-substituted phenyl moieties exhibited excellent activity (hyperalgesia 27% inhibition at 20mg/kg, $ED_{50}$ value 20 mg/kg).[17]

114

# References

1. Iyer V B, Gurupadayya B, Koganti V S, Inturi B, Chandan R S. Design, synthesis and biological evaluation of 1, 3, 4-oxadiazoles as promising anti-inflammatory agents. Med Chem Res. 2017;26(1):190-204.

2. Foot O, Malaviya A. Treatment of rheumatoid arthritis: current and future. Future Presc. 2013;14(2):8-12.

3. M'koma A E. Inflammatory bowel disease: an expanding global health problem. Clin Med Insights Gastroenterol. 2013;6:S12731.

4. Abdelazeem A H, Habash M, Maghrabi I A, Taha M O. Synthesis and evaluation of novel diphenylthiazole derivatives as potential anti-inflammatory agents. Med Chem Res. 2015;24(10):3681-3695.

5. Narayana B, Raj K V, Ashalatha B V, Kumari N S, Sarojini B K. Synthesis of some new 5-(2-substituted-1, 3-thiazol-5-yl)-2-hydroxy benzamides and their 2-alkoxy derivatives as possible antifungal agents. Eur J Med Chem. 2004;39(10):867-872.

6. Ali Y, Alam M S, Hamid H, Husain A, Dhulap A, Hussain F, Bano S, Kharbanda C. Molecular modeling and synthesis of some new 2-imino-4-thiazolidinone derivatives with promising TNF-α inhibitory activity. New J Chem. 2016;40(1):711-723

7. Lin T A, McIntyre K W, Das J, Liu C, O'Day K D, Penhallow B, Hung C Y, Whitney G S, Shuster D J, Yang X, Townsend R. Selective Itk inhibitors block T-cell activation and murine lung inflammation. Biochem. 2004;43(34):11056-11062.

8. Ge L, Hu Q, Shi M, Yang H, Zhu G. Design and discovery of novel thiazole derivatives as potential MMP inhibitors to protect against acute lung injury in sepsis rats via attenuation of inflammation and apoptotic oxidative stress. RSC Advances. 2017;7(52):32909-32922.

9. Helal M H M, Salem M A, El-Gaby M S A, Aljahdali M. Synthesis and biological evaluation of some novel thiazole compounds as potential anti-inflammatory agents. Eur J Med Chem. 2013;65:517-526.

10. Miwatashi S, Arikawa Y, Kotani E, Miyamoto M, Naruo K I, Kimura H, Tanaka T, Asahi S, Ohkawa S. Novel inhibitor of p38 MAP kinase as an anti-TNF-α drug: discovery of N-[4-[2-ethyl-4-(3-methylphenyl)-1, 3-thiazol-5-yl]-2-pyridyl] benzamide (TAK-715) as a potent and orally active anti-rheumatoid arthritis agent. J Med Chem. 2005;48(19):5966-5979.

11. Kim E A, Han A R, Choi J, Ahn J Y, Choi SY, Cho S W. Anti-inflammatory mechanisms of N-adamantyl-4-methylthiazol-2-amine in lipopolysaccharide-stimulated BV-2 microglial cells. Int Immuno pharmacol. 2014;22(1):73-83.

12. Koppireddi S, Komsani J R, Avula S, Pombala S, Vasamsetti S, Kotamraju S, Yadla R. Novel 2-(2, 4-dioxo-1, 3-thiazolidin-5-yl) acetamides as antioxidant and/or anti-inflammatory compounds. Eur J Med Chem. 2013;66:305-313.

13. Kouatly O, Eleftheriou P, Petrou A, Hadjipavlou-Litina D, Geronikaki A. Docking assisted design of novel 4-adamantanyl-2-thiazolylimino-5-arylidene-4-thiazolidinones as potent NSAIDs. SAR and QSAR Environ Res. 2018;29(2):83-101.

14. Ramagiri R K, Vedula R R, Thupurani M K. A facile one-step multi-component approach toward the synthesis of 3-(2-amino-4-thiazolyl) coumarins by using trimethylsilylisothiocyanate and their antioxidant and

anti-inflammatory    activity. Phosphorus    Sulfur    Silicon    Relat Elem. 2015;190(9):1393-1397.

15. Sharma R N, Xavier F P, Vasu K K, Chaturvedi S C, Pancholi S S. Synthesis of 4-benzyl-1, 3-thiazole derivatives as potential anti-inflammatory agents: an analogue-based drug design approach. J Enzyme Inhib Med Chem. 2009;24(3):890-897.

16. Wang S M, Zha G F, Rakesh K P, Darshini N, Shubhavathi T, Vivek H K, Mallesha N, Qin H L. Synthesis of benzo [d] thiazole-hydrazone analogues: molecular docking and SAR studies of potential H+/K+ ATPase inhibitors and anti-inflammatory agents. Med Chem Commun. 2017;8(6):1173-1189.

17. Carter P H. Progress in the discovery of CC chemokine receptor 2 antagonists, 2009–2012. Expert Opin Ther Pat. 2013;23(5):549-568.

# Chapter-7

## Anti-oxidant activity of 2-aminothiazoles

In living organism oxidation is natural and essential process for the production of energy in biological processes. Reactive oxygen species (ROS) like hydroxyl,peroxide and nitric oxide radicals which are produced throughout the immoderate metabolism in living being sand cause oxidative injury to the normal cells and leads to degenerative disease associated with age, cancer, diabetes, cardiovascular and wide-ranging human diseases.[1,2]Anti-oxidants are any substance which significantly inhibits or delay the oxidation of substrate and are may be of natural and synthetic in origin. The major action of antioxidants is used to prevent cells from damaging due to reactive oxygen species and they also provide electrons that neutralize free radicals which have potential to cause degenerative and life threatening diseases.[3]

A new series of N2- [2-chloro-4(3,4,5-trimethoxy phenyl azetidin-1-yl]-N4-(substituted aryl)-1,3-thiazol-2,4-diamine was synthesized by Jaishree et al. and evaluated for in vitro anti-oxidant properties. Compounds **115a**, **115b** and **115c** displayed highest anti-oxidant activity towards lipid peroxide at $IC_{50}$ value of 11 $\pm0.45$, 18 $\pm0.09$ and 21 $\pm0.17$ µg/ml whereas compounds **115d** and **115e** displayed reasonable inhibitory potential with $IC_{50}$ value of 24 $\pm0.07$ and 38 $\pm0.08$ µg/ml.[1]

| Comp. | R | R$_1$ | R$_2$ | R$_3$ |
|-------|-----|-----|-----|-----|
| 115a | -OCH$_3$ | -OCH$_3$ | -OCH$_3$ | -NHC$_6$H$_4$COOH |
| 115b | -OCH$_3$ | -OCH$_3$ | -OCH$_3$ | -NHC$_6$H$_4$C$_2$H$_5$ |
| 115c | -OCH$_3$ | -OCH$_3$ | -OCH$_3$ | -NHC$_6$H$_4$COOC$_2$H$_5$ |
| 115d | -OCH$_3$ | -OCH$_3$ | -OCH$_3$ | -NHC$_6$H$_4$OH |
| 115e | -OCH$_3$ | -OCH$_3$ | -OCH$_3$ | -NHC$_6$H$_4$ |

115 (a-e)

A series of N-(substituted phenyl)-N'-(naphtha[1,2-d] thiazol-2-yl) urea and thiourea derivatives was reported by Azamet et al. and screened for anti-parkinsonian and anti-oxidant potential (Azamet et al., 2008). Compounds **116a**, **116b**, **116c** and **116d** diminished the catalepsy and oxidative stress which was found by treating the animal with haloperidol. Compounds **116a, 116b, 116d, 116e** and **116f** also exhibited excellent anti-cataleptic activity.[4]

| Comp. | R | X |
|-------|---|---|
| 116a | 2-OCH₃ | O |
| 116b | 2,4-OCH₃ | O |
| 116c | 2-OCH₃ | S |
| 116d | 2-NO₂ | S |
| 116f | 3,4,5-OCH₃ | O |
| 116e | 2-NO₂ | O |

116 (a-f)

A new series of phenylpropenes methoxylated cinnamaldehydes and their new Schiff bases was reported by the Sharma et al. (2013) and studied for anti-oxidant as well as antimicrobial activity. Compound **117a** exhibited highest in vitro antioxidant activity with 80.71% inhibition where as other compounds with thiazole-based Schiff bases displayed antibacterial activity towards *B. subtilis* (**117b**; MIC 0.12mM), *M. luteus* and *S. aureus* (**117c**; MIC 0.20mM).[5]

| Comp. | R |
|-------|---|
| 117a | p-ClC₆H₃ |
| 117b | H |
| 117c | C₆H₄ |

117 (a-c)

Bonacorso et al. (2016) reported a novel series of trifluoromethyl substituted N-(pyrimidin-2-yl) Benz[d]thiazol-2-amines and investigated for anti-oxidant activity. Compounds **118a** and **118b** displayed more potent anti-oxidant activity whereas compounds **118c** and **118d** exhibited the valuable antioxidant activity.[6]

| Comp. | R₁ | R₂ |
|-------|----|----|
| 118a | H | H |
| 118b | H | CH₃ |
| 118c | -(CH₂)₄- | - |
| 118d | 4-CH₃-C₆H₄ | H |

118 (a-d)

A new series of photoactive 4-(4-chlorophenyl)-2-(1H-indol-3-yl)-6-substituted phenyl-2H-thiazolo[3,2-a] [1,3,5] triazines reported by Sravanthi et al. (2015) and synthesized by the condensation of 4-chlorobenzaldehyde and indole-3-carbaldehyde Schiff bases via theaddition of ammonia. The compound **119** having ortho hydroxyl group displayed excellent anti-oxidant activity with high fluorescence intensity.[7]

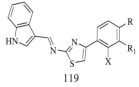

| Comp. | R | R₁ | X |
|-------|---|----|----|
| 119 | H | H | OH |

119

Reddy et al. (2015) synthesized a novel series of thiourea, selenourea and urea derivatives having thiazole moiety and investigated for in vitro anti-oxidant activity using nitric oxide, hydrogen peroxide radical scavenging and 1, 1-diphenylpicrylhydrazyl methods. The derivatives were synthesized by nucleophilic addition reaction of various substituted isothiocyanates/isocyanates /isoselenocynates with (2-amino-4-(3 chlorophenyl) thiazol-5-yl) (2-chlorophenyl) methanone in acetone having sodium hydroxide as catalyst. Compounds such as **120a, 120b, 120c** and **120d** displayed most promising anti-oxidant activity.[8]

| Comp. | R | X |
|-------|---|---|
| 120a | CH₃ | Se |
| 120b | OCH₃ | Se |
| 120c | Br | Se |
| 120d | F | Se |

120 (a-d)

Shidore et al. (2016) synthesized a new series of hybrid compounds by combining the benzylpiperidine fragment of vicinal diarylthiazole and donepezil and evaluated its anticholinesterase (anti-ChE) activity as well as anti-oxidant activity. The particular hybrid diarylthiazole– benzylpiperidine derivatives came up with compound **121** exhibiting the highest anti-oxidant and anticholinesterase potential with $IC_{50}$ value of $0.30 \pm 0.01$ μM.[9]

| Comp. | R | X | X |
|-------|---|---|---|
| 121 | 3,5-diF | Me | Me |

121

A novel series of 4-(3-nitrophenyl) thiazol-2-ylhydrazone analogues were reported by Carradori et al. (2017) and evaluated for its anti-oxidant as well as anti-Parkinson's activity and compound **122** displayed highest anti-oxidant activity.

*Mode of Action*-Compound **122** showed high inhibition potential against monoamine oxidase B (MAO-B) enzyme. Molecular docking study also explained that compound displayed strong binding interaction with monoamine oxidase enzyme (PDB: 2V5Z).[10]

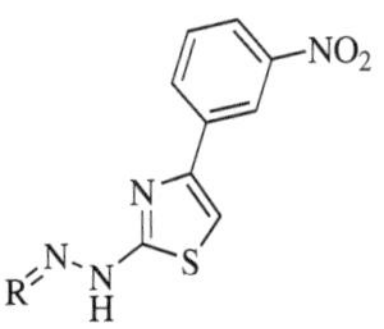

| Comp. | R |
|-------|---|
| 122 | 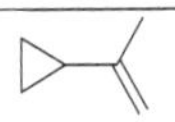 |

122

A new series of monoazo disperse dyes skeleton gave 2-amino-N-(5-arylthiazol-2-yl) selenopheno- (pyridine, pyridazine and quinoline)-2-acetamide reported by Khalifa et al. and prepared via the condensation of various 2-(N-chloroacetyl)-5-arylazo-thiazole with seleno- (pyridazine, pyridine and quinoline) carbonitrile analogues. Compounds were investigated for various activities like antioxidant, anticancer and antibacterial and found that compounds **123a**, **123b**, **123c** and **123d** displayed most potent antioxidant activity.[11]

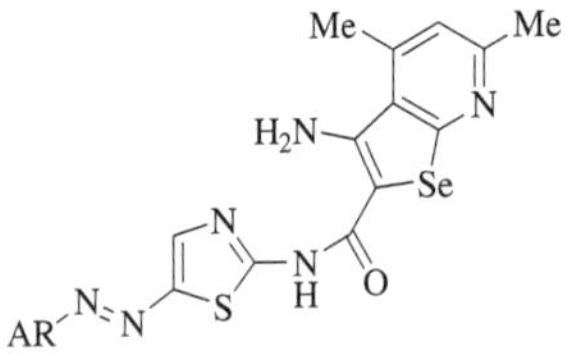

123a

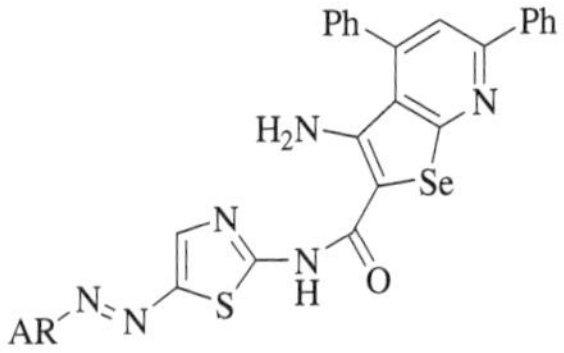

123 (b-d)

| Comp. | Ar | Comp. | Ar |
|-------|----|----|----|
| 123a | Ph | 123c | 4-CH$_3$-Ph |
| 123b | Ph | 123d | 4-NO$_2$-Ph |

Kumar et al. (2018) prepared an innovative series of α-amino phosphonates and screened for its antioxidant potential. The synthesis of α-aminophosphonates proceeded through an intermediate imine by the Kabachnik-Field reaction under solvent free condition at room temperature in the presence of nano-$BF_3.SiO_2$, an efficient solid acid. Compound **124a** having a 4-fluorophenyl moiety and **124b** having a 3-chloro-4-fluorophenyl ring displayed highest antioxidant activity.[12]

| Comp. | R |
|-------|---|
| 124a | (4-fluorophenyl)CHO |
| 124b | (3-chloro-4-fluorophenyl)CHO |

124 (a-b)

# References

1. Jaishree V, Ramdas N, Sachin J, Ramesh B. In vitro antioxidant properties of new thiazole derivatives. J Saudi Chem Soc. 2012;16(4):371-376.

2. Sivakumar K K, Rajasekharan A, Buggareddy S. Synthesis, characterization, in-vitro anti-oxidant and cytotoxic activity of n-mannich bases of 5-amino-4-[2-(6-bromo-1, 3-benzo thiazol-2-yl) hydrazinylidene]-2, 4-dihydro-3h-pyrazol-3-one. Int J Res Pharm Chem. 2012;2:32.

3. Hazra K, Nargund LV, Rashmi P, ChandraNS J N, Nandha B. Synthesis and antioxidant activity of some novel Fluorobenzothiazolopyrazoline. Der ChemicaSinica. 2011;2(2):149-157.

4. Azam F. Synthesis of some urea and thiourea derivatives of naphtha [1, 2-d] thiazol-2-amine as anti-Parkinsonian agents that cause neuroprotection against haloperidol-induced oxidative stress in mice. Med Chem Res. 2009;18(4):287-308.

5. Sharma U K, Sood S, Sharma N, Rahi P, Kumar R, Sinha A K, Gulati A. Synthesis and SAR investigation of natural phenylpropene-derived methoxylatedcinnamaldehydes and their novel Schiff bases as potent antimicrobial and antioxidant agents. Med Chem Res, 2013;22(11):5129-5140.

6. Bonacorso H G, Calheiro T P, Rodrigues M B, StefanelloS T, Soares F A, Zanatta N, Martins M A. Eco-friendly synthesis and antioxidant activity of new trifluoromethyl-substituted N-(pyrimidin-2-yl) benzo [d] thiazol-2-amines and some N-derivatives. Monatsh Chem. 2016;147(12): 2185-2194.

7. Sravanthi T V, Manju S L. Synthesis and fluorescence properties of novel indol-3yl-thiazolo [3, 2-a] [1, 3, 5] triazines and indole-3-carbaldehyde schiff bases. J Fluoresc. 2015;25(6):1727-1738.

8. Bhaskara R M V, Srinivasulu D, Peddanna K, Aarao C, Ramesh P. Synthesis and antioxidant activity of new thiazole analogues possessing urea, thiourea, and selenourea functionality. Synth Commun. 2015;45(22):2592-2600.

9. Shidore M, Machhi J, Shingala K, Murumkar P, Sharma M K, Agrawal N, Tripathi A, Parikh Z, Pillai P, Yadav M R. Benzylpiperidine-linked diarylthiazoles as potential anti-Alzheimer's agents: synthesis and biological evaluation. J Med Chem. 2016;59(12):5823-5846.

10. Carradori S, Ortuso F, Petzer A, Bagetta D, De Monte C, Secci D, De Vita D, Guglielmi P, Zengin G, Aktumsek A, Alcaro S. Design, synthesis and biochemical evaluation of novel multi-target inhibitors as potential anti-Parkinson agents. Eur J Med Chem. 2018;143: 1543-1552.

11. Khalifa M E, Abdel-Hafez S H, Gobouri A A, Kobeasy M I. Synthesis and biological activity of novel arylazothiazole disperse dyes containing selenium for dyeing polyester fibers. Phosphorus SulfurSilicon Relat Elem. 2015;190(4):461-476.

12. Kumar G S, Prasad Y R, Mallikarjuna B P, Chandrashekar S M. Synthesis and pharmacological evaluation of clubbed isopropylthiazole derived triazolothiadiazoles, triazolothiadiazines and mannich bases as potential antimicrobial and antitubercular agents. Eur J Med Chem. 2010; 45(11):5120-5129.

# Chapter-8

## Anticancer activity of 2-aminothiazoles

Cancer is characterized by abnormal cells which grows uncontrollably and 2nd principle reason of death and accounting for 8.8 million deaths in 2015. In low and middle earning countries, around 70% peoples die from cancer. In India, approximately 2.5 million peoples are suffering with this disease and above seven lakh patients get registered every year. The initiation and progression mechanism of cancer has been well ascertained but still the efficacious treatment of cancer endure a vast challenge facing the scarcity of early detection, indeterminate tumor cell dormancy status and metastatic properties of malignant tumor.[1] Conventional cytotoxic chemotherapeutics available which include antimetabolites, alkylating agents, tubulin-targeting inhibitors and topoisomerase inhibitors, target cancer cells by interfering with DNA integrity or cell division having severe side effects.[2] Thus, the recognition of novel drugs having cytotoxic potential with fewer side effects and a broad spectrum of activity is desirable to ameliorate cancer treatment. Thiazole-2-amine derivatives were found to have cytotoxic potential towards various cell lines and one of the oral marketed drug is Dasatinib under brand name is Sprycel and act by inhibiting a number of tyrosine kinases such as Bcr-Abl and the Src kinase family. It is used to cure chronic myelogenous leukemia.

Dasatinib

Sun et al. (2017) presented N,4-diaryl-1,3-thiazole-2-amine analogues and evaluated for its antiproliferative potential as tubulin inhibitors against (SGC-7901) gastric adenocarcinoma cells, (A549) lung adenocarcinoma cells and (HT-1080) fibrosarcoma cells. Compound **125** N-(2,4-dimethoxyphenyl)-4-(4-methoxyphenyl)-1,3-thiazol-2-amine exhibited the most potent antiproliferative activity. The 2,4-dimethoxy substitution was responsible for anticancer potential while halogen substituted compounds showed moderate activity and methyl and acetyl substitution at N position of 2-aminothiazole resulted in decrease in activity.

*Mechanism of action-* Compound **125**was also accessed for tubulin polymerization inhibition assay and exhibited comparing activity with CA-4 and found to interfere with microtubule polymerization by formation of abnormal mitotic spindle. Molecular docking study also shown that compound **125** effectively binds with colchicine binding site of tubulin (PDB: 3HKD).[3]

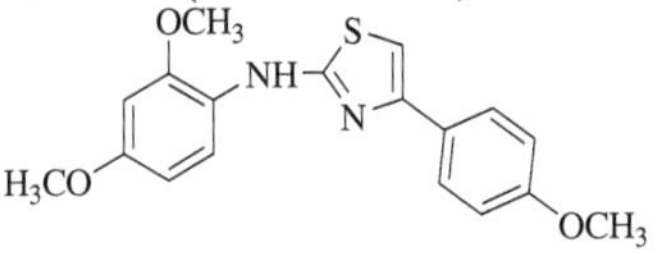

125

Honshuang et al. (2016) synthesized 2-aminothiazole derivatives with various hydrophobic substitutions at $4^{th}$ or $5^{th}$ position of main core structure such as bromo, methyl, phenyl or butylidene and evaluated their cytotoxic potential against HI299 (cell line: human lung cancer), SHG-44 (cell line: human glioma cancer). Compounds **126 (a-e)** were found to exhibit antitumor potential against both cancer cell lines. The SAR study revealed that methyl substitution cause decreased in potency while replacement of methyl with bromo group cause enhancement in potential.[1]

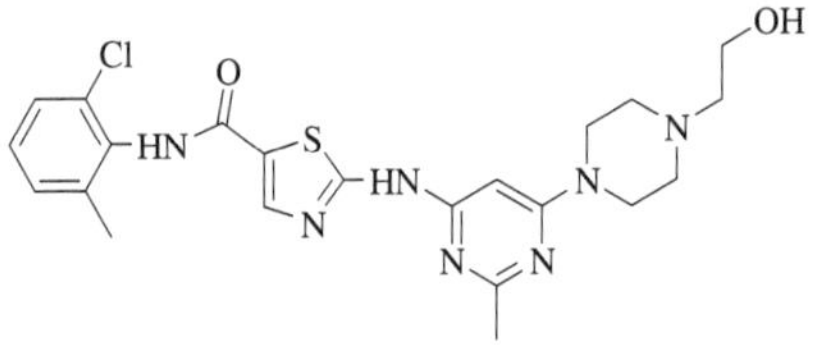

126 (a-e)

| Comp. | R | R₁ | N | Comp. | R | R₁ | n |
|-------|----|-----|---|-------|----|-----|---|
| 126a | Br | 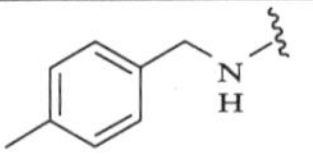 | 1 | 126d | Br | 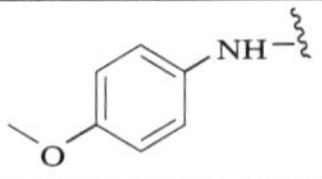 | 1 |
| 126b | Br | 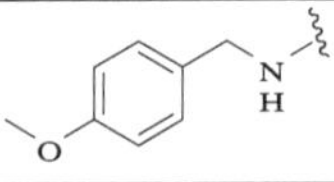 | 1 | 126e | Br | 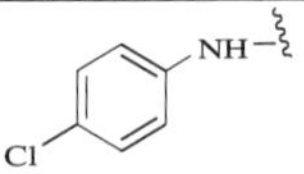 | 1 |
| 126c | Br | 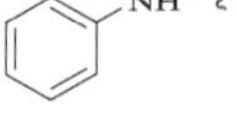 | 1 | | | | |

Ali et al. (2013) synthesized a series of acetamides having both 2-imino-4-arylthiazoles and morpholine or different piperazine analogues and screened for their anticancer potential against 60 different human cancer cell lines. Compounds **127a** and **127b** were found to have more cytotoxic potential and even showed promising result in case of druglikeness study, drug score profile and estimation of toxicity. Cytotoxicity evidenced by affinity of synthesized compounds towards DNA topoisomerase 2-alpha is demonstrated by following order like arylpiperazine series>methylpiperazine series>morpholine series>phenylpiperazine series.[4]

127a                      127b

Kuramoto et al., 2008 synthesized 2-(2-aminothiazol-4-yl) benzo[b]furan and 3-(2-aminothiazol-4-yl) benzo[b]furans and evaluated them for its leukotriene B4 (LTB4) and growth inhibitory activity in cancer cell lines. Compound **128a** exhibited excellent inhibition of BLT2 receptor while compound 128b displayed growth inhibitory activity towards MIA PaCa-2(cell line: human pancreatic cancer). Both of these compounds were found to have common structural feature 2-[(dimethylamino)methylene amino] thiazole bearing substituent at 5th position.[5]

128a                      128b

Chen et al., 2016 synthesized 2-amino-N-(2-aminophenyl) thiazole-5-carboxamide analogues and evaluated cytotoxic potential against K562 (cell line: human leukemia) and DU145 (cell line: prostate cancer) Compounds **129a, 129b, 129c** showed the highest activity towards both cell lines.

*Mechanism of action-* These compounds displayed antiproliferative activity as Bcr-Abl (protein kinase) and histone deacetylase (HDACs) dual inhibitors. The 2-aminothiazole ring of designed and synthesized compounds occupied ATP binding pocket of Abl same as Dasatinib.[6]

| Comp. | $R_1$ | $R_2$ |
|-------|-------|-------|
| 129a | | H |
| 129b | | H |
| 129c | | F |

El-Messery et al., 2012 synthesized a new series of 2-acetamido and 2 or 3-propanamido analogues of 4- or 5-substituted-thiazoles and tested them for their anticancer potential. Compounds **130**, **131** and **132** displayed broad spectrum antiproliferative activity against diverse cancer cell lines. It was established that compounds having aromatic phenyl substitution favored the activity as compared to aliphatic substituted thiazoles.[7]

130    131

132

## References

1. Li H, Wang X, Duan G, Xia C, Xiao Y, Li F, Ge Y, You G, Han J, Fu X, Tan S. Synthesis, antitumor activity and preliminary structure-activity relationship of 2-aminothiazole derivatives. Chem Res Chinese U. 2016;32(6): 929-937.

2. Tadesse S, Zhu G, Mekonnen L B, Lenjisa J L, Yu M, Brown M P, Wang S. A novel series of N-(pyridin-2-yl)-4-(thiazol-5-yl) pyrimidin-2-amines as highly potent CDK4/6 inhibitors. Future Med Chem. 2017;9(13):1495-1506.

3. Sun M, Xu Q, Xu J, Wu Y, Wang Y, Zuo D, Guan Q, Bao K, Wang J, Wu Y, Zhang W. Synthesis and bioevaluation of N, 4-diaryl-1, 3-thiazole-2-amines as tubulin inhibitors with potent antiproliferative activity. PloS one. 2017;12(3): e0174006.

4. Ali A R, El-Bendary E R, Ghaly M A, Shehata I A. Novel acetamidothiazole derivatives: synthesis and in vitro anticancer evaluation. Eur J Med Chem. 2013;69: 908-919.

5. Kuramoto M, Sakata Y, Terai K, Kawasaki I, Kunitomo J I, Ohishi T, Yokomizo T, Takeda S, Tanaka S, Ohishi Y. Preparation of leukotriene B4 inhibitory active 2-and 3-(2-aminothiazol-4-yl) benzo [b] furan derivatives and their growth inhibitory activity on human pancreatic cancer cells. Org Biomol Chem. 2008;6(15): 2772-2781.

6. Chen X, Zhao S, Wu Y, Chen Y, Lu T, Zhu Y. Design, synthesis and biological evaluation of 2-Amino-N-(2-aminophenyl) thiazole-5-carboxamide derivatives as novel Bcr-Abl and histone deacetylase dual inhibitors. RSC Advances. 2016;6(105):103178-103184.

7. El-Messery S M, Hassan G S, Al-Omary F A, El-Subbagh H I. Substituted thiazoles VI. Synthesis and antitumor activity of new 2-acetamido-and 2 or 3-propanamido-thiazole analogs. Eur J Med Chem. 2012;54: 615-625.

## About the Authors

**Dr. Vikramjeet Singh** is currently working as Assistant Professor in Department of Pharmaceutical Sciences, Guru Jambheshwar University of Science and Techno-logy, Hisar. He has 30 research publications in national and international reputed journals. He has guided 09 M. Pharm. students for their M. Pharm. dissertation and one candidate is pursuing Ph.D. under his supervision. He has attended many national and international conferences. He has been working as a reviewer for various international journals.

**Ms. Samridhi Thakral** pursuing Ph.D. at Department of Pharmaceutical Sciences, Guru Jambheshwar University of Science and Technology, Hisar. She has 4 research papers in her credit.

**Mr. Pankaj Bishnoi** did M. Pharm. from Department of Pharmaceutical Sciences, Guru Jambheshwar University of Science and Technology, Hisar.

Printed in Great Britain
by Amazon